Disclaimer

All material on Peapil.com and this book is provided for your information only and may not be construed as medical advice or instruction. No action or inaction should be taken based solely on the contents of this information; instead, readers should consult appropriate health professionals on any matter relating to their health and well-being. If you think you may have a medical emergency, call your doctor or 911 immediately.

The content of this book (text, graphics and images) is not intended to be a substitute for professional medical advice, diagnosis, or treatment. Always seek the advice of your physician or other qualified health provider with any questions you may have regarding a medical condition.

Never disregard professional medical advice or delay in seeking it because of something you have read in this book. The information and opinions expressed here are believed to be accurate, based on the best judgment available to the authors. Readers who fail to consult with appropriate health authorities assume the risk of any injuries. Reliance on any information and content provided by Peapil Publishing and this book is solely at your own risk.

The publisher is not responsible for errors or omissions.

ISBN 978-1-9995720-2-0

ISBN 978-1-9995720-2-0   US$27.95

5 2 7 9 5 >

9 781999 572020

Rev 2.2

INTRODUCTION TO THE MEDITERRANEAN LIFESTYLE

I know... I know... It's called the Mediterranean Diet. But I hate that word... diet. It sounds like you're going to have to stop eating all your favorite foods, start calorie counting, or join some cult-like exercise place... Really! It's been used for decades to describe some pretty horrific things.

But—have no fear.

This book isn't about dieting, calorie counting, or anything like that. It's about adopting a lifestyle that's been around for hundreds of years. A lifestyle full of delicious, seasonal and fresh foods. The Mediterranean Diet is full of an unlimited amount of food from all nutritional groups. Although there are different focuses that you may be unfamiliar with, no food groups are completely excluded. There are no hard and fast rules; just "Less of this" and "More of this" guidelines.

The diet is based on the eating habits of people on the coasts of Italy, Morocco, Spain, Greece and France. People living on the shores of the Mediterranean have a very healthy diet because of the abundance of heart-healthy foods found right outside their doors: foods like fresh fish, nuts, and fruit. Imagine going on a Mediterranean vacation... you get to eat like this every day. Including... yes—a little bit of wine!

This isn't the typical restrictive North American "diet".

The Mediterranean Diet is widely acknowledged as one of the healthiest diets in the world. And for the money, when making a list of the most healthy and delicious diets, this is the best one in the world bar none.

People in the Mediterranean (that haven't succumbed to a McDonald's-heavy diet) have reduced risk of heart disease. The diet is associated with a lower level of oxidized low-density lipoprotein (LDL) cholesterol. This is the "bad" cholesterol that is likely to build up deposits in your arteries.

By eating the Mediterranean Diet, a study of nearly 26,000 women found that those who followed this type of diet had 25% less risk of developing cardiovascular disease over the course of 12 years.[1] This means they were less likely to die from heart-related diseases and lived longer overall. Following the guidelines of a Mediterranean Diet resulted in lower levels of inflammation, blood sugar, and body mass index—all of which are the primary drivers of increased heart disease risks when their levels are too high.

One myth that these studies have debunked is that by just eating "low-fat" foods you could reduce the risk of heart disease. As you'll discover, the Mediterranean diet actually encourages eating fats—but good-for-you fats. That means lots of extra virgin olive oil and nuts. The risk of diabetes was also decreased by eating Mediterranean foods.[2]

Eating more olive oil and mixed nuts has also been shown to reduce breast cancer. The healthy fats you get from the Mediterranean Diet have also been linked to decreasing the likelihood of cancer, Parkinson's and even Alzheimer's. The same study also found that women who followed the Mediterranean Diet were 46% more likely to age healthfully. Eating plants, whole grains, fish, and even a bit of red wine... plus skipping processed foods —it's a great way to get past 70 years old without developing chronic diseases or declines in mental health.[3]

Getting the fresh foods, healthy fats and natural sugars—as opposed to our typical processed, artificial, sugar-choked diet—leads to a longer, more productive life with less fear of mental and physical illnesses in the future.

The Mediterranean Diet has been recommended by the American Heart Association as a great way to try and prevent cardiac diseases.[4] And that's one of the primary reasons so many people turn to this lifestyle.

But the benefits of the Mediterranean Diet don't only happen as you age. You'll notice (and feel) some of the changes almost immediately.

IMMEDIATE BENEFITS OF THE MEDITERRANEAN DIET

✔ Detoxed liver and colon

✔ Curbed sugar cravings

✔ Boosted energy levels

✔ Finding and maintaining ideal weight

✔ Fighting inflammation

✔ Making blood sugar management easy

WHY I GOT INVOLVED

My name is **Erika Simons** and I'm currently the head recipe coach over at *Mediterranean Refresh*! I joined the team there because it was created specifically for people like me and you who want to transform our bodies and lives.

I'm a mother and a daughter who has first-hand experience with the disastrous results of our processed, unnatural, sugar-filled lifestyles.

I wouldn't be the woman I am today if it wasn't for my mother. I owe her so much. I'm sure many of you can relate.

She was an incredible chef who trained under some of the best culinary minds in California, and she taught me everything she knew about cooking. By the time I was a teenager, she had taught me how to make authentic dishes from places like Japan, Italy, Greece, and so many others.

The only trouble was, even though my mom could create meals that people happily paid hundreds of dollars for, she struggled with her weight and more importantly, her health.

As a young girl, I watched her battle with an eating disorder.

While my family and I would eat the incredible dinners she cooked for us, she seemed only to push food around her plate with a fork, never taking a bite.

That was until I turned 14 and everything changed.

Her dietary habits were unsustainable, and her body didn't know what to make of the food she was eating.

This was the year my mom was put into the hospital for the first time. She was never able to bring herself to eat the kinds of foods that would properly nourish her, and it took a severe toll on her health and our entire family.

So, for months at a time, we would visit her in the hospital.

Over the span of three years her health rapidly declined—until she passed away in May of 2003.

It was at this point, after the loss of my mother, that I decided to take a stand and change my life.

This was all because of the standard American diet...

I decided I would never again eat anything that could threaten my chance to love my children for as long as possible. I was tired of being tired, overweight and headed down the same path as my mom.

So, from that point forward, healthy cooking became the key to unlocking my best possible life.

After reading about the problems caused by our typical diet, I became obsessed.

Surely, the longevity of a people indicated how good their overall diet is. So, I started researching different cultures. Which ones had the lowest rates of heart disease, Alzheimer's disease, and Parkinson's disease? Where were people naturally lean and energetic?

During my hunt I discovered dozens of cultures with longer lives and less illness. It was true: Our diets affect our lives more than we care to admit.

But... there was a problem.

So many of these "healthy" diets were based on restrictive eating. Eating small amounts of bland, tasteless food. As a recipe developer, I consider delicious food as an essential part of life.

If you told me I'd live longer if I chose not to be a mother... I would tell you to get lost. A short life full of joy is better than a long one.

This is less extreme than that example... but it remains true. I **need** to eat delicious food. I'd rather die than eat bland, tasteless food all my life. It's just part of my soul.

That's when I stumbled on the Mediterranean Diet. My research indicated that it was in fact one of the best lifestyles in the world based on longevity and reduced incidence of disease. And... when I explored the diet in more depth, I discovered just how delicious the food can be.

I decided to give it a shot.

I didn't have any recipes, and no idea how to get started.

But little by little, I started to feel a lot better.

I felt refreshed... energized! I was sleeping easier, and I had zero brain fog in the morning. After just a couple weeks....

I started spending more time with my children again. I was even more active at work!

It took months, but I eventually developed a whole catalogue of recipes to choose from. I started adapting my favorite American recipes to fit into the Mediterranean Diet. I adapted traditional Mediterranean recipes to make them easier to make. I only chose ingredients I could find at the local supermarket.

In time, I became really proficient as a Mediterranean chef, and my friends and family started asking me for healthy recipes constantly. Every day, I see how the recipes I adapt and create are changing lives. My friends and family all have slimmer waistlines, higher energy, deeper sleep, and feel better overall.

But friends and family kept asking me for the recipes. And after a while, I got tired of constantly writing out each recipe.

So, I started looking into publishing and that's when I bumped into the Peapil Publishing team. They helped work with me to develop the wonderful recipes you see in this book today. All of these recipes are approved for the Mediterranean Diet and contain no artificial ingredients.

1. Ahmad S, Moorthy MV, Demler OV, Hu FB, Ridker PM, Chasman DI, Mora S. Assessment of Risk Factors and Biomarkers Associated With Risk of Cardiovascular Disease Among Women Consuming a Mediterranean Diet. *JAMA Network Open*. 2018

2. Salas-Salvadó J, Bulló M, Babio N, Martínez-González MÁ, Ibarrola-Jurado N, Basora J, Estruch R, Covas MI, Corella D, Arós F, Ruiz-Gutiérrez V. Reduction in the incidence of type 2 diabetes with the Mediterranean diet. *Diabetes care*. 2011

3. Samieri C, Sun Q, Townsend MK, Chiuve SE, Okereke OI, Willett WC, Stampfer M, Grodstein F. The Association Between Dietary Patterns at Midlife and Health in Aging: An Observational Study. *Annals of internal medicine*. 2013

4. Mediterranean Diet. www.heart.org. https://www.heart.org/en/healthy-living/healthy-eating/eat-smart/nutrition-basics/mediterranean-diet. Published 2019. Accessed January 14, 2019.

ESSENTIAL ELEMENTS OF THE MEDITERRANEAN DIET

In a nutshell, the Mayo Clinic states this diet...

"[Emphasizes eating] primarily plant-based foods, such as fruits and vegetables, whole grains, legumes and nuts. Replacing butter with healthy fats such as olive oil and canola oil. Using herbs and spices instead of salt to flavor foods."

The diet doesn't require eliminating fat from your diet. Many trending food lifestyles like Keto and Paleo actually recommend fat... and this diet is no different. It's overall a less restrictive diet that believes in fresh foods, whole grains, and legumes.

USE OLIVE OIL

Olive oil is the primary source of fat in this diet. It provides monounsaturated fat—a type that reduces LDL (bad) cholesterol levels. We recommend "extra-virgin" because it has the highest levels of the plant compounds that actually provide antioxidant effects.

Recent research indicates that olive oil protects against developing chronic diseases and helps with diabetes, obesity and cancer. It has a cardioprotective role; providing an anti-hypertensive, antithrombotic, antioxidant, anti-inflammatory and anti-carcinogenic action.

The diet isn't about limiting total fat consumption, but rather making good choices about which fats to consume. To fully feel the effects of this dietary lifestyle, avoid saturated fats and hydrogenated oils which have trans fats. These unhealthy fats are tied to heart disease and will counteract all of the healing that your body is undergoing.

EAT LOTS OF FISH!

Don't worry—even if you're not a fish lover, there's plenty of delicious recipes to experiment with. Fish are rich sources of omega-3 fatty acids.

The fish is cooked fresh and is never deep-fried. Don't worry, there are plenty of directions in the recipe section of this book.

WINE TIME

The health effects of wine have been debated forever. But most experts agree that as long as you don't drink excessively, wine can be a wonderful component of your diet. If you choose to drink wine, we recommend limiting your consumption to 5 ounces per day for those over 65 and 10 ounces per day for those under 65.

GO NUTS

Nuts contain the beneficial linolenic acid (a type of omega-3 fatty acid). Omega-3 fatty acids lower triglycerides, decrease blood clotting, are associated with decreased sudden heart attack, improve the health of your blood vessels, and help moderate blood pressure.

Nuts are another vital food group in the diet. Nuts are high in fat but most of the fat is not saturated. Make sure not to eat too many, about a handful a day. And avoid the corner store candied nuts. I recommend unsalted nuts and love fresh walnuts, acorns and almonds. Cashews are also a tasty choice.

Replacing your regular snacks with nuts is a great way to reduce empty calories, added sugar and sodium. Nuts are also a great source of fiber and minerals like potassium. Much better than processed snack foods.

EAT VEGGIES AND FRUIT

Make sure to always include a handful of veggies in every dish you prepare. Don't be afraid to eat a piece of fruit or add it to a recipe for an extra bit of natural sweetness. In general, use fruit instead of adding sugar. One of the best parts of this diet is hitting up the local farmer's markets and choosing what to eat based on the seasons. It's a wonderful way to educate my children and they love going!

Rule of thumb: Eat veggies all day long... for every meal. It's simply the best way to get extra nutrients, fill your tummy without a ton of calories, and is actually proven to reduce stress.

Fruits are the best way to satisfy your sweet tooth. Because the sugar is naturally occurring and the fruit has fiber, it won't spike your blood sugar nearly as badly as the same amount of added sugar. Full of vitamin C and antioxidants, fruits are a great way to complete a well-balanced diet.

SWITCH TO WHOLE GRAINS

This is such a simple way to increase fiber and nutrition in your diet. I always recommend whole grains for a delicious guilt-free pasta dish.

Grains in the Mediterranean region are typically whole grain and contain very little trans fats. Bread is important to the diet but is never eaten with butter or margarines, which we avoid because they contain trans fats.

CHOOSE OLIVE OIL AND SKIP BUTTER

Olive oil makes a wonderful alternative to butter. We also have a wonderful tahini you can use as a dip or spread. Butter is not necessarily bad for you but compared to olive oil it has more saturated fats and less monounsaturated fat.

LESS RED MEAT

Substitute fish and poultry for red meat. When you do choose red meat, try to make the portions small. And always opt for fresh meat over preserved or processed meats like sausage and jerky.

LOW-FAT, NO-SUGAR DAIRY

We recommend low–fat yogurt with no added sugar. It's an easy way to get all the benefits of dairy without the baggage.

ADD SPICES

Spices are full of nutrients and anti-inflammatory properties. Not to mention they can make any dish ten times more delicious. When going through the recipes, take note of which spices and herbs we recommend. Try to get good at knowing how much you like to add, and which ones are your favorite. Try to reduce the amount of added sugar you need to improve the recipes.

LIVING BETTER WITH THE MEDITERRANEAN DIET

The Mediterranean Diet can help you achieve your weight goals or keep a stable healthy weight. However, the strongest point in the diet is its ability to help avoid heart disease.

TIPS FOR SUCCESS

Before you get started on the diet, it's good to do a little bit of preparation. Oftentimes we jump right into things... and it's easy to get overwhelmed. So, read on a bit and study this before jumping into the recipes (unless you just need something fun to eat, then feel free to pick a recipe and get started!).

ADAPT YOUR CURRENT DIET

Before jumping into the diet completely, just take a look at what you currently eat and try and make subtle changes. Reduce the red meat, change the oil to olive oil. Try switching to low-fat yogurt. Reduce the number of sugary treats. Try to morph your current diet into the Mediterranean Diet instead of starting from scratch. Slowly moving towards this diet will make it harder to move back to your old ways.

Learn to make some simple substitutions. Instead of eating a bag of chips, grab a fistful of nuts. Find something in the Mediterranean Diet that will make a healthy replacement for all your current eating habits.

I've included a whole section on snack foods, drinks, and even desserts to help you on your path. Take a look at those sections right now and think about which recipes there would be a great substitute for your current habits.

YOUR NEW FOOD PYRAMID

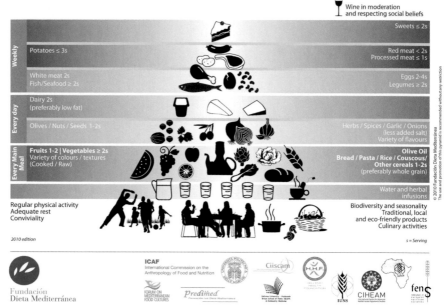

Mediterranean Diet Pyramid: a lifestyle for today
Guidelines for Adult population

Serving size based on frugality and local habits

Wine in moderation and respecting social beliefs

Weekly
Sweets ≤ 2s
Potatoes ≤ 3s
Red meat < 2s
Processed meat ≤ 1s
White meat 2s
Fish/Seafood ≥ 2s
Eggs 2-4s
Legumes ≥ 2s

Every day
Dairy 2s
(preferably low fat)
Olives / Nuts / Seeds 1-2s
Herbs / Spices / Garlic / Onions
(less added salt)
Variety of flavours

Every Main Meal
Fruits 1-2 | Vegetables ≥ 2s
Variety of colours / textures
(Cooked / Raw)
Olive Oil
Bread / Pasta / Rice / Couscous /
Other cereals 1-2s
(preferably whole grain)

Water and herbal infusions

Regular physical activity
Adequate rest
Conviviality

Biodiversity and seasonality
Traditional, local
and eco-friendly products
Culinary activities

2010 edition

s = Serving

© 2010 Fundación Dieta Mediterránea
The use and promotion of this pyramid is recommended without any restriction

Fundación
Dieta Mediterránea

ICAF
International Commission on the
Anthropology of Food and Nutrition

FORUM ON MEDITERRANEAN FOOD CULTURES

Predimed

Ciiscam

H.H.F.

CIHEAM

IUNS

fenS

This food pyramid was developed by The Mediterranean Diet Foundation Expert Group and shows what foods you should eat as part of the diet. Each recipe in this book closely follows this pyramid.

Here's an example of the Mediterranean Food Pyramid:

Fresh Fruits and Vegetables, 4+ servings

Try to opt for fresh, seasonal fruits and veggies. If you're ever hungry, just know you can eat more veggies!

Fats, 4–6 servings

Whole Grains, 3–5 servings

Seafood 1 serving

Dairy Products 1 serving

Red Wine 5 ounces per day

Meat 2–5 servings per week

Always opt for poultry over red meat, but still only eat small serving sizes.

THE PANTRY

In order to maintain the diet, it's important to stock up on some common ingredients that most of these recipes will share. That way you're not running to the grocery store every day! I made sure each recipe in this book uses common ingredients, so you're not running to specialty shops to try and find an obscure ingredient for a single recipe. No special equipment or appliances are needed.

Don't leave temptations in sight! Everything you buy at the grocery store will end up in your belly... so just leave the bag of chips there. It's so much harder to avoid indulgence when the food is right there... waiting to be eaten. And you have to! How often have you heard yourself say, "I wouldn't eat this, but it's going to go bad... so I have to!"? It happens so often to me.

Take a good look at your pantry and fridge. With the directions I gave you earlier in this book, try to give away or toss out some unhealthy ingredients. I know it can be hard. It seems like a big waste of money. But the benefits of making a clean switch to this healthier way of living is way more valuable than the unhealthy food you need to get rid of.

This includes getting rid of your less healthy oils and margarine. Make sure to stock up on lots of great olive oil.

ENJOY THE VACATION

Take your time. Remember when I said the Mediterranean Diet is like eating as if you're on vacation? One of the core tenets of the diet is to take things slowly when eating. Instead of shoving food down as quickly as possible after going through a drive-thru or mindlessly eating while paying attention to Netflix, we invite you to sit down at the table with your family and friends. Slowly enjoy and savor what you're eating.

Gathering with friends and family and enjoying a freshly made meal is a vital part of the Mediterranean culture. Even without friends, enjoying a meal with your loved ones— talking about the day and enjoying each other's presence... it's so amazing.

Not only will you enjoy the food better, eating slowly allows you to pay attention to your stomach. It's good to get an awareness of when you're truly full to prevent overeating. Taking smaller portion sizes is the easiest way to reduce weight.

Be prepared to stop eating when you're satisfied... so often we end up eating until we need to start undoing our belts! Really pay attention while you eat slowly—take notes on what changes you'd like to make to the recipe in the future.

ARGH... EXERCISE

No lifestyle book is complete without a little blurb about exercise. Thankfully, if you go to our online community, you'll find dozens of resources that will help people just like you get into a more active lifestyle. I invite you to visit that community today!

www.Peapil.com/MediteranneanRefresh

Try to get about 20 minutes of exercise every day. One "cheat" I use is to always take the stairs. I also make sure to park far away from the entrance when I go to the grocery store.

Little things like this force you to get a bit of exercise in. I've also tried to get more involved with my daughter's activities. Instead of sending her to dance class, I actually joined a Mom/Daughter class so we can dance together! It's so much more fun than just watching her dance, I get to learn with her... and get some exercise!

HOW TO EAT OUT

When eating out, take care to pick a place where you're sure to get fresh and not fried food. If you do happen to slip up and get fast food, don't beat yourself up. Even being a full-time recipe developer... I sometimes end up with a sloppy burger in my hands! It's not going to kill you... just make sure it doesn't ruin your trend.

Lean more towards seafood places, farm-to-table restaurants, and Italian, Spanish, and Greek restaurants. Vegetarian restaurants are also a great choice! That said, most restaurants have plenty of Mediterranean-style choices.

Avoid anything fried, and make sure to ask if you're not sure. Choose from the poultry or vegetarian options. Beef dishes are typically the most calorie laden. Be very careful with sauces and dressings. I typically ask for mine on the side. Try to avoid creamy sauces and ask for vinaigrette instead.

Most restaurants are used to substitutions due to allergies and dietary restrictions, so don't be afraid to tell them what you're unable to eat. For example, ask to sub regular marinara sauce for that alfredo you're about to order. Make sure to ask for extra veggies!

Side dishes are an easy place to slip up... but it's also an easy to place to make huge improvements. Instead of fries, upgrade to that salad. Drinks are also an easy place to make a mistake. A glass of red wine or sparkling water is a great alternative to sugary sodas and beer.

Don't be afraid to pack up your food for later. In fact, you should almost never finish a full meal at a restaurant. Restaurants are designed to make people satisfied... no matter their appetite. Think about me for a second. I'm not a very tall woman... but the restaurant will serve the meal in the same size as my over six-foot-tall husband!

I recommend skipping dessert for the most part. Unless they have a fruit bowl, opt for a tea or coffee. If skipping just isn't an option... make sure to split the dish with your partner.

SOME ADVICE ON BEING SUCCESSFUL – WHAT TO EAT

The reason I turned to the Mediterranean Diet isn't just because it's extremely healthy... many diets are. But unlike most diets, I believe this one is full of foods you will enjoy. There's a wonderful variety of foods with very few forbidden choices. Really, it's just a shift in the amount you eat. There's no need to count calories if you eat properly and stop when you're satisfied.

Within just a few days, you'll be looking forward to your meals. Not just for the taste, but also for the feeling you get after you're finished eating. Feeling refreshed, not bloated. Satisfied, not stuffed. Energetic, not sluggish. You'll sleep better, have less brain fog... and rest easy knowing you're contributing to a healthy heart and brain.

The Mediterranean Diet is based in large part on eating a hearty amount of fresh produce including fruits and vegetables. Whole grains are eaten at most meals along with seafood several times a week. Meat is eaten only in small portions, and not terribly often either.

Substitute olive oil for all your other oils and butters. Try to avoid all creamy sauces and dressings. When available, opt for vinaigrettes and tomato-based sauces. Clear, broth-based soups are also great! But avoid chunky, sodium filled soups.

SHOPPING GUIDE

Every ingredient in this book can be sourced at your local grocery store. But I definitely recommend exploring your local shops. Find the best fishmonger to go to. Check out your favorite butcher. And make sure to pick up seasonal fruits and veggies from your farmer's market. Bread should come from your local bakery, if they serve whole wheat. Make sure to talk to these people; they're often highly knowledgeable about food and will make recommendations based on your diet and aspirations.

I highly recommend making ingredient substitutions based on what you can find locally! When shopping at the grocery store, stay away from prepackaged foods. Try to stick to the fresh food aisles. The freezer section can be handy for grabbing food that is currently out of season.

It may be difficult at first to figure out your shopping routine but begin to take note of where ingredients are kept, and you'll be in and out of the grocery store in no time.

THANK YOU

Before I let you dive into the recipes, I just want to thank you for picking up and reading this book. It means so much to me that you've decided to incorporate my recipes into your life.

Enjoy! And I can't wait to see you in the community.

Erika Simons

1. Mediterranean Diet. www.heart.org. https://www.heart.org/en/healthy-living/healthy-eating/eat-smart/nutrition-basics/mediterranean-diet. Published 2019. Accessed January 14, 2019.
2. Buckland G, Gonzalez CA. The role of olive oil in disease prevention: a focus on the recent epidemiological evidence from cohort studies and dietary intervention trials. - PubMed - NCBI. Ncbi.nlm.nih.gov. https://www.ncbi.nlm.nih.gov/pubmed/26148926. Published 2019. Accessed January 14, 2019.

BREAKFAST

Recipes

BREAKFAST
Fig Smoothie

This rich and creamy fig smoothie is a great way to start your day, particularly if you need something quick and easy. This smoothie not only tastes delicious but will also assist balancing energy levels as it is full of both complex carbohydrates and good quality healthy fats. Figs are also known as the fruits of the Gods and are full of fiber, vitamins, minerals and antioxidants, all of which are going to help support our overall health and wellbeing.

Serves: 2		
4	Lg	Fresh figs, cut in quarters
2	Sml/Med	Frozen bananas, sliced
1	Tbsp	Chia seeds
3	Tbsp	Oats
3	Tbsp	Almonds
¼	Cup	Natural Greek yogurt
1 ½	Cup	Water
2	Tbsp	Honey
1	Cup	Ice

1. Add all the ingredients to a high speed blender and process on high for 1 minute or until smooth. Add more liquid if necessary to adjust thickness and blend again.

2. Divide between two tall glasses and serve immediately.

Data for 1 serving:

Calories	470 kcal		**Cholesterol**	3 mg
Total Carbohydrates	81 g		**Sodium**	41 mg
Protein	11 g		**Potassium**	915 mg
Total Fat	15 g		**Dietary Fiber**	12 g
Saturated Fat	2 g		**Sugar**	57 g
Polyunsaturated Fat	3 g		**Vitamin A**	6% Daily Value
Monounsaturated Fat	7 g		**Vitamin C**	19% Daily Value
Trans Fat	0 g		**Calcium**	51% Daily Value
			Iron	14% Daily Value

CAPRESE
Breakfast Tart

Do you have a few mouths to feed at breakfast time, or perhaps hosting a special brunch? This Caprese Breakfast Tart is a wonderful option as a slice-and-share meal that everyone is going to love. The classic flavors of tomato, cheese and fresh basil works well together, so well in fact that there is no need to add to it or make it any more complicated– (if it's not broken, don't fix it).

This simple, yet impressive breakfast dish can be served either hot or cold… Whichever way it will be gone before you know it.

Serves: 8			
1	Lg	Sheet Puff pastry	
2	Tbsp	Olive oil	
36	Slices	Tomato, sliced thin	
36	Slices	Fresh mozzarella, (fresh buffalo milk) sliced thin	
¼	Cup	Parmesan, freshly grated	
¼	Cup	Basil, fresh leaves torn	

1. Line a baking tray with non-stick paper.
2. Lay out flat the puff pastry sheet on top of the baking paper. Lightly brush the pastry with 1 tablespoon of the olive oil.
3. Lay out three rows of 12 cheese slices and 12 tomato slices, alternating as you go and overlapping slightly, ensuring you leave a ½ to 1-inch gap/border around all sides.
4. Once all three rows are done, drizzle over the remaining olive oil and sprinkle over the parmesan cheese.
5. Bake in the oven for 30–35 minutes or until golden.
6. Remove from the oven and sprinkle over the fresh basil leaves. Slice and serve immediately.

Data for 1 serving:

Calories	377 kcal	**Cholesterol**	40 mg
Total Carbohydrates	17 g	**Sodium**	190 mg
Protein	19 g	**Potassium**	191 mg
Total Fat	28 g	**Dietary Fiber**	1 g
Saturated Fat	9 g	**Sugar**	2 g
Polyunsaturated Fat	7 g	**Vitamin A**	15% Daily Value
Monounsaturated Fat	6 g	**Vitamin C**	15% Daily Value
Trans Fat	0 g	**Calcium**	24% Daily Value
		Iron	6% Daily Value

COTTAGE CHEESE
Blueberry Casserole

When having this Cottage Cheese Blueberry Casserole for breakfast, you may just think that you're having dessert instead. Don't be fooled. While it is absolutely delicious, this meal is also loaded with protein and low in sugar, which makes this recipe a great option to start the day. Next time you're wanting to go to a little extra effort and create something special for your morning meal, give this dish a go. Leftovers (unlikely to be any though) can be served for a snack or even an after dinner "treat." Enjoy!

Serves: 6

4		Eggs, separated
½	tsp	Salt
2	Tbsp	Lemon juice, freshly squeezed
1	tsp	Vanilla extract
1	tsp	Almond extract
⅔	Cup	Monk fruit sweetener, (or natural sugar of choice)
⅔	Cup	Spelt flour, sifted
2	tsp	Lemon peel, finely grated
2	Cup	Cottage cheese
1	Cup	Sour cream
1 ½	Cup	Blueberries, (fresh or frozen)

1. Preheat oven to 300 F and lightly grease a casserole dish. Set aside.
2. In a medium bowl, beat the egg yolks until light. Blend in the salt, lemon juice, vanilla, almond extract, sweetener, spelt flour and lemon peel.
3. Place the cottage cheese into a large bowl, add a small amount of egg yolk mixture and beat on high speed until curd is broken and nearly smooth.
4. Add remaining egg yolk mixture and sour cream. Beat until blended.
5. In a separate bowl, beat egg whites until stiff but not dry, and then fold into cheese mixture.
6. Pour into the greased casserole dish. Place in oven and bake for 40 minutes.
7. Remove from the oven and sprinkle the blueberries on top, in an even layer. Continue to bake for another 20 minutes. Refrigerate at least 5 hours before serving. Best to make the night before and allow to chill overnight for breakfast in the morning.

Data for 1 serving:

Calories	244 kcal	**Cholesterol**	165 mg	
Total Carbohydrates	41 g	**Sodium**	542 mg	
Protein	18 g	**Potassium**	134 mg	
Total Fat	10 g	**Dietary Fiber**	2 g	
Saturated Fat	6 g	**Sugar**	29 g	
Polyunsaturated Fat	1 g	**Vitamin A**	11%	Daily Value
Monounsaturated Fat	2 g	**Vitamin C**	9%	Daily Value
Trans Fat	0.6 g	**Calcium**	11%	Daily Value
		Iron	8%	Daily Value

Breakfast Pizza

Pizza for breakfast? Yes please!

This recipe for Breakfast Pizza uses a simple dough that is quick and easy to make with no need for a lengthy proving time. Topped to the brim with plenty of your favorite breakfast ingredients, this is essentially a "Big Breakfast" or "Breakfast with the Works," just made into a pizza, (genius, right?).

Serve the pizza in the middle of the table and watch it quickly disappear. If you have a few mouths to feed we suggest you double the batch. This will make sure you will get a slice of your own to enjoy before it's all gobbled up.

Serves: 4		
1 ½	Cup	Self-raising flour, plus more for kneading
1	Cup	Plain Greek yogurt
2	Tbsp	Olive oil
½	Cup	Arugula leaves
⅓	Cup	Mushrooms, sliced
¼	Cup	Cream cheese
5	Slices	Prosciutto, chopped
3		Eggs
⅓	Cup	Parmesan cheese, freshly grated
		Salt and pepper, to taste

1. Preheat oven to 500 F.
2. In a mixing bowl, mix together the flour and the yogurt, using your hands if required.
3. Tip out onto a floured flat surface and knead together for approximately 10 minutes using more flour as necessary.
4. Lightly grease a 12-inch pizza pan and spread the dough (starting from the center) to the edges of the pan.
5. Parbake in oven for 6 minutes, until the base just begins to brown. Remove from oven and add your toppings.
6. Spread the olive oil over the base and then sprinkle with the arugula and mushrooms.
   Drop cream cheese one teaspoon at a time and then arrange the prosciutto in an even fashion on top of the pizza.
7. Carefully crack the eggs on top of the pizza, towards the center so they do not run off the edge. Sprinkle with parmesan cheese and a good crack of salt and pepper.
8. Bake for an additional 10 to 15 minutes or until toppings are thoroughly heated, eggs are cooked to your liking and crust is deep golden brown.
9. Slice and serve immediately.

Data for 1 serving:

Calories	428	kcal	Cholesterol	174	mg
Total Carbohydrates	40	g	Sodium	1142	mg
Protein	19	g	Potassium	335	mg
Total Fat	21	g	Dietary Fiber	1	g
Saturated Fat	8	g	Sugar	5	g
Polyunsaturated Fat	2	g	Vitamin A	9%	Daily Value
Monounsaturated Fat	9	g	Vitamin C	1%	Daily Value
Trans Fat	2.3	g	Calcium	39%	Daily Value
			Iron	17%	Daily Value

FRUIT SALAD
with Italian Ricotta

This is no ordinary fruit salad. The addition of Italian ricotta balances the flavors in this fruit salad perfectly. The walnuts also add a little texture while the cranberries give a subtle tang to the dish which is divine. This impressive breakfast dish is surprisingly simple and can be tossed together in no more than 10 minutes (with time to spare). If you're needing to eat on the run you can simply combine your salad together in a mason jar to make this the perfect portable breakfast.

Serves: 4		
2	Lg	Apples, cored and thinly sliced
2	Lg	Nashi pears, cored and thinly sliced
1	Cup	Fresh baby spinach leaves
⅓	Cup	Dried cranberries
⅓	Cup	Walnuts, finely chopped
⅔	Cup	Italian ricotta
2 ½	Tbsp	Honey, raw
½	Tbsp	Lemon juice, freshly squeezed
½	tsp	Ground cinnamon

1. In a salad bowl, toss together the sliced apples, pears, spinach leaves, dried cranberries and finely chopped walnuts.

2. In a separate bowl, whip together the Italian ricotta, honey, lemon juice and cinnamon. Toss through the salad and serve immediately.

Data for 1 serving:

Calories	309 kcal	**Cholesterol**	48 mg
Total Carbohydrates	27 g	**Sodium**	125 mg
Protein	15 g	**Potassium**	295 mg
Total Fat	17 g	**Dietary Fiber**	3 g
Saturated Fat	8 g	**Sugar**	16 g
Polyunsaturated Fat	4 g	**Vitamin A**	17% Daily Value
Monounsaturated Fat	4 g	**Vitamin C**	10% Daily Value
Trans Fat	1.7 g	**Calcium**	30% Daily Value
		Iron	5% Daily Value

GOLDEN
Millet Porridge

How awesome is it to start your day with a bowl of warm, comforting porridge? This porridge recipe may be a little different than what you may have grown up with. We have swapped the oats for millet and added a few Mediterranean-inspired ingredients. This Golden Millet Porridge is packed full of goodness, is nutrient dense and promotes many health benefits. Not only is it good for your health, it will also do wonders for your soul as it is the ultimate comfort breakfast meal.

Serves: 4

Porridge:

1 ½	Cup	Millet, uncooked
½	Cup	Apple, cored and diced
½	Cup	Butternut squash, diced
3	Cup	Milk, of choice
2	Cup	Water
½	tsp	Ground cinnamon
¼	tsp	Sea salt

To serve:

2	Tbsp	Honey
4	Tbsp	Walnuts, roughly chopped
4	Tbsp	Raisins
1	pinch	Ground cinnamon

1. Place all porridge ingredients in a large saucepan and bring to a boil.
2. Cover and reduce heat, allow to simmer until liquid is absorbed and millet, squash and apple are tender, approximately 25 minutes.
3. To serve, divide porridge between serving bowls. Drizzle with a little honey, a sprinkle of walnuts and raisins and a pinch of ground cinnamon. Feel free to also add a dash of milk if you wish.

Data for 1 serving:

Calories	512	kcal	Cholesterol	18	mg
Total Carbohydrates	83	g	Sodium	226	mg
Protein	16	g	Potassium	539	mg
Total Fat	14	g	Dietary Fiber	8	g
Saturated Fat	4	g	Sugar	24	g
Polyunsaturated Fat	6	g	Vitamin A	32%	Daily Value
Monounsaturated Fat	3	g	Vitamin C	8%	Daily Value
Trans Fat	1.4	g	Calcium	24%	Daily Value
			Iron	15%	Daily Value

GOURMET
Feta Toast

Toast for breakfast is a firm favorite for many families; however, it can quickly become a little boring, particularly if all you're spreading on it each morning is jam or honey. Mix things up a little and create some excitement around breakfast by adding a a gourmet touch to your simple sliced toast.

The flavor of the feta cheese, goes perfectly with the tomato and avocado, while the squeeze of citrus and the sprinkle of pomegranate ariels bring flavors that pop and impress. Feel free to use your preferred style of bread to toast; however, sourdough does go beautifully.

Makes: 4		
4	slices	Toast, of choice (rye/sourdough/multigrain)
½	Cup	Greek feta, soft
2	Sml	Tomatoes, thinly sliced
1		Avocado, thinly sliced
2	Tbsp	Pepitas
4	Tbsp	Pomegranate ariels
2	Tbsp	Flaxseed sprouts (optional)
4		Lemon (or lime) wedges

1. Prepare your toast according to your liking. Once done, transfer slices to serving plates.
2. Spread each slice of toast with the feta cheese. Top with the slices of tomato and avocado, then sprinkle over the pepitas, pomegranate ariels and flaxseed sprouts if using.
3. Serve immediately with a lemon or lime wedge to squeeze over the top.

Data for 1 serving:

Calories	223 kcal		**Cholesterol**	11 mg
Total Carbohydrates	22 g		**Sodium**	318 mg
Protein	7 g		**Potassium**	372 mg
Total Fat	12 g		**Dietary Fiber**	5 g
Saturated Fat	3 g		**Sugar**	3 g
Polyunsaturated Fat	2 g		**Vitamin A**	12% Daily Value
Monounsaturated Fat	6 g		**Vitamin C**	26% Daily Value
Trans Fat	0.3 g		**Calcium**	5% Daily Value
			Iron	8% Daily Value

LEMON

Ricotta Pancakes

Many people would have fond memories of growing up, sharing in a plate of pancakes for breakfast on a special occasion. Next time you're whipping up a batch of pancakes, whether it be for a birthday breakfast or a weekend treat, give these Lemon Ricotta Pancakes a try. We promise you will love them, and they just might become one of your new favorites.

Best served warm with latherings of butter, a squeeze of lemon juice and a dusting of sugar, you may want to cook up a double batch as everyone will keep coming back for more.

Makes: Approximately 6 Large		
⅔	Cup	Ricotta cheese
2	Lg	Eggs, separated
¼	Cup	Milk (of choice)
6	Tbsp	Whole wheat flour
2	tsp	Sugar
¼	tsp	Baking powder
⅛	tsp	Salt
1	Tbsp	Lemon peel, finely minced
1	tsp	Lemon verbena*, finely minced
2	tsp	Olive oil

* If you are unable to source lemon verbena, substitute another lemon scented herb such as lemon balm, lemon basil or lemon thyme (or a combination of all).

1. The night before, place the cheese in a cheese cloth (muslin cloth) or use a paper coffee filter and set in a strainer over a bowl, cover with plastic wrap, and refrigerate. In the morning, discard the whey collected in the bowl.

2. Add the drained ricotta to a food processor or blender with the egg yolks and process until smooth.

3. Add milk, flour, sugar, baking powder, and salt and process until completely blended.

4. Fold in lemon rind and lemon verbena.

5. Beat egg whites in mixing bowl until just stiff but still moist, and then fold gently into batter.

6. Heat 2 teaspoons of olive oil in large nonstick skillet over medium heat. Drop batter by ¼ cupfuls onto skillet and cook until tops bubble. Turn and cook second side until golden brown.

7. Repeat with remaining batter.

8. Serve immediately with your favorite toppings such as lemon juice with a dusting of sugar or a drizzle of fresh local honey.

Data for 1 serving:

Calories	135 kcal		**Cholesterol**	89 mg
Total Carbohydrates	11 g		**Sodium**	122 mg
Protein	6 g		**Potassium**	79 mg
Total Fat	8 g		**Dietary Fiber**	1 g
Saturated Fat	3 g		**Sugar**	3 g
Polyunsaturated Fat	0.5 g		**Vitamin A**	6% Daily Value
Monounsaturated Fat	2 g		**Vitamin C**	2% Daily Value
Trans Fat	2.5 g		**Calcium**	10% Daily Value
			Iron	4% Daily Value

OVERNIGHT
Breakfast Strata

This breakfast meal is a fantastic recipe to prepare ahead of time and makes the ideal family breakfast. This Strata is warming, nourishing and full of Mediterranean inspired flavors and perfect for when the mornings begin to get a little cooler. Feel free to make ahead of time, either the night before, ready for the next morning, or pop it in the freezer for the days/weeks to come. Just make sure it is well defrosted before baking.

Leftovers can also become a fantastic lunch or even dinner option, making this meal a great all-round family dish.

Serves: 6

12		Sourdough bread slices, cubed
1	lb	Ground pork
⅓	Cup	Onion, peeled and chopped
⅓	Cup	Green pepper, seeded and chopped
4	oz	Pimiento jar, drained and chopped
6	Lg	Eggs
3	Cup	Milk
½	Cup	Feta, cubed
2	tsp	Worcestershire sauce
1	tsp	Dry mustard
½	tsp	Sea salt
¼	tsp	Pepper
2	tsp	Oregano, fresh

1. Lightly grease a 9"×13" baking pan or casserole dish and sprinkle in the bread cubes, set aside.
2. In a skillet, brown the ground pork with the onion and green pepper; drain off any excess fat.
3. Stir in pimientos and then sprinkle the pork and vegetable mixture over the bread.
4. In a bowl, beat together the eggs, milk, feta, Worcestershire sauce, mustard, salt, pepper and oregano and carefully pour over sausage mixture. Cover and refrigerate overnight.
5. The next day, remove the strata from the fridge and allow to come to room temperature.
6. Bake, covered, at 325 F for 1 hour and 20 minutes.
7. Uncover and bake 10 minutes longer or until a knife inserted near the center comes out clean.
8. Let stand for 10 minutes before serving.

Data for 1 serving:

Calories	426 kcal		**Cholesterol**	57 mg
Total Carbohydrates	42 g		**Sodium**	695 mg
Protein	20 g		**Potassium**	349 mg
Total Fat	17 g		**Dietary Fiber**	1 g
Saturated Fat	8 g		**Sugar**	6 g
Polyunsaturated Fat	1 g		**Vitamin A**	11% Daily Value
Monounsaturated Fat	7 g		**Vitamin C**	33% Daily Value
Trans Fat	0.9 g		**Calcium**	16% Daily Value
			Iron	16% Daily Value

PISTACHIO
Olive Bread

The thought of making bread from scratch can overwhelm some people; however, this bread recipe is not your typical bread recipe. In fact, bread recipes don't get much easier than this. This recipe calls for you to simply add everything to one bowl, mix then bake. No setting aside to rise, pound, knead, rise again and so on. Simply mix, bake and devour! With the addition of pistachios and olives, this bread oozes a beautiful Mediterranean vibe. Slice while still warm, spread with a little butter and try not to eat it all at once.

Makes: 1 loaf
Servings: 12

1 ½	Cup	Flour
1	Tbsp	Sugar, (optional)
2 ½	tsp	Baking Powder
½	tsp	Salt
¾	Cup	Milk
¼	Cup	Olive Oil
2		Eggs
⅓	Cup	Pistachios, shelled and chopped
3	Tbsp	Greek olives, pitted and chopped

1. Preheat oven to 350 F.
2. Grease and flour an 8–½" loaf pan.
3. In a medium sized bowl stir and toss together the flour, sugar (if used), baking powder and salt; set aside.
4. In a small bowl whisk together the milk, oil and eggs until smooth. Stir in the pistachios and olives.
5. Add to the combined dry ingredients and stir just until blended.
6. Spread evenly in the prepared pan and bake until a thin wooden skewer inserted in the center of the loaf comes out clean, approximately 50 minutes.
7. Cool in the pan for 10 minutes, then turn out onto a wire rack to cool completely.

Data for 1 serving:

Calories	160 kcal	Cholesterol	33 mg	
Total Carbohydrates	16 g	Sodium	280 mg	
Protein	4 g	Potassium	84 mg	
Total Fat	9 g	Dietary Fiber	1 g	
Saturated Fat	1 g	Sugar	2 g	
Polyunsaturated Fat	1 g	Vitamin A	1%	Daily Value
Monounsaturated Fat	5 g	Vitamin C	11%	Daily Value
Trans Fat	0.5 g	Calcium	8%	Daily Value
		Iron	7%	Daily Value

SPANISH

Breakfast Beans

This rich and hearty Spanish-inspired break-fast dish is both extremely flavorsome and nourishing. This dish offers warmth and depth and will quickly become a breakfast favorite. If you are pressed for time in the mornings, this dish can be made a day or two ahead as it reheats well. In fact, we think it tastes even better when made ahead as it allows extra time for the rich flavors to develop. Serve on top of a slice of toast or alongside a crusty baguette. A sprinkle of shaved parmesan and fresh parsley on top would go nicely too.

Serves: 4

2	Cup	Chicken or vegetable stock
1	Sml	Potato, diced
½	Med	Bell pepper, seeded and finely diced
1 ½	tsp	Garlic powder
2	Tbsp	Sofrito
1	tsp	Sazon, or a little more to taste
3	Tbsp	Tomato sauce
14	oz	Canned pinto beans

To serve:

		Lemon juice, freshly squeezed to taste
		Salt and pepper, to taste
		Crusty bread or toast

1. Place all ingredients in medium saucepan and boil until the vegetables are tender and cooked, approximately 20 minutes.
2. Season with salt and pepper to taste, and a squeeze of lemon juice.
3. Serve over crusty bread or toast.

Data for 1 serving:

Calories	150 kcal	**Cholesterol**	0 mg
Total Carbohydrates	23 g	**Sodium**	697 mg
Protein	7 g	**Potassium**	306 mg
Total Fat	2 g	**Dietary Fiber**	6 g
Saturated Fat	0.02 g	**Sugar**	4 g
Polyunsaturated Fat	0.1 g	**Vitamin A**	15% Daily Value
Monounsaturated Fat	0.005 g	**Vitamin C**	66% Daily Value
Trans Fat	2 g	**Calcium**	5% Daily Value
		Iron	10% Daily Value

STUFFED
Mushrooms

These Stuffed Mushrooms are super easy to make, delicious and a fantastic way to start the day. Stuffed full of vegetables, this breakfast meal will ensure you are properly fueled to tackle anything coming your way that day. These mushrooms are not only a great meal option, they are also a celebration of simple, Mediterranean flavors that go perfectly together on a plate. If you want to take this recipe to another level, you can also serve with a little shaved parmesan cheese, either melted or sprinkled as-is over the top.

Serves: 4		
8	Lg	Portobello mushrooms
3	Tbsp	Olive oil
1		Onion, peeled and finely diced
1		Garlic clove, minced
1		Zucchini, finely diced
1		Bell pepper, seeded and finely diced
2		Tomatoes, finely diced
3	Tbsp	Chives, freshly chopped
½	Tbsp	Lemon juice, freshly squeezed
		Salt and pepper, to taste

1. Pre-heat oven to 350 F.
2. Wipe mushrooms clean and remove stems (save for another use).
3. Lightly oil baking sheet with 2 tablespoons of oil and lay mushrooms on it stalk side up.
4. Pour ½ tsp of olive oil over each one and bake for 20–30 minutes.
5. Meanwhile heat the remaining olive oil in a non-stick skillet over medium heat.
6. Add the onion and garlic and sauté for 5 minutes. Add the zucchini and bell pepper and continue to sauté for 10–15 minutes until soft. Add in the diced tomatoes and chives, cook for a further 5 minutes and then season the vegetables with the lemon juice, salt and pepper to taste.
7. Remove the mushrooms from the oven and fill each mushroom cap with the vegetable mixture and serve.

Data for 1 serving:

Calories	194 kcal	**Cholesterol**	0 mg
Total Carbohydrates	18 g	**Sodium**	33 mg
Protein	9 g	**Potassium**	318 mg
Total Fat	11 g	**Dietary Fiber**	9 g
Saturated Fat	2 g	**Sugar**	7 g
Polyunsaturated Fat	1 g	**Vitamin A**	28% Daily Value
Monounsaturated Fat	8 g	**Vitamin C**	107% Daily Value
Trans Fat	0 g	**Calcium**	2% Daily Value
		Iron	2% Daily Value

TORTILLA
Española

This Tortilla Española is a traditional Spanish omelette and is full of vibrant, rich Mediterranean flavors. We're not sure if the best part of this omelette is the delicious taste and how filling it is, or if it's the fact it's all made in one pan (saves on washing up) and is super easy to make. We guarantee you will love it just as much for whichever reason, or perhaps a reason of your own.

If you don't mind going to a little extra effort (or creating more dishes for yourself), you could also transfer your Tortilla Española mixture to 4 individual ramekins before placing in the oven to cook. This is a great option for serving individual portions for each person.

Serves: 4

2	Tbsp	Olive oil
2	Sml/Med	Potatoes, scrubbed and diced
1		Onions, peeled and sliced thin
1		Italian sausage, sliced
3		Garlic cloves, minced
1	Sml/Med	Red bell pepper, seeded and sliced
6		Eggs, beaten
		Salt and pepper, to taste

1. In a large cast iron skillet or Dutch oven, heat the olive oil over medium heat.
2. Sauté potatoes, sausages, onions and garlic over low to medium heat until the potatoes are soft, onions are translucent and sausage is cooked through.
3. Add in the slices of bell pepper and toss through.
4. In a bowl, beat the eggs well and season with salt and pepper.
5. Pour the eggs over the potatoes and sausages in the skillet and swirl around so the eggs coat the pan evenly.
6. Place the cast iron skillet in the oven and bake for approximately 20 minutes or until cooked through. When the middle is set and the top is slightly brown, it's done.
7. Remove from oven and allow to sit for 5 minutes. Run a knife around the outside and invert onto a round platter. Serve at room temperature.

Data for 1 serving:

Calories	455 kcal		Cholesterol	52 mg
Total Carbohydrates	20 g		Sodium	1123 mg
Protein	19 g		Potassium	631 mg
Total Fat	33 g		Dietary Fiber	3 g
Saturated Fat	10 g		Sugar	3 g
Polyunsaturated Fat	4 g		Vitamin A	25% Daily Value
Monounsaturated Fat	16 g		Vitamin C	93% Daily Value
Trans Fat	0.2 g		Calcium	3% Daily Value
			Iron	10% Daily Value

LUNCH

Recipes

CARPACCIO

Recipes don't get much easier than this.... In fact it is hardly a recipe as such, more of an arrangement. The trick with this recipe is to place the beef fillet in the freezer to become a little hard/firm so it can be sliced paper-thin. The slices of beef served with the zesty sauce, arugula, and shaved parmesan served on top of either fresh bread or toasted baguette is the perfect meal to serve up as a shared plate in the warmer months when you're trying to escape the heat.

Serves: 4

1	lb	Beef filet
½	Cup	Olive oil
½	Cup	Lemon juice
¼	Cup	Red wine*
1	Tbsp	Shallots, minced
2	Tbsp	Capers, drained
1	Sml	Garlic clove, minced
1	Tbsp	Prepared mustard
2	Tbsp	Parsley, chopped
		Salt
¼	Cup	Arugula leaves
2	Tbsp	Parmesan, freshly shaved

1. Trim all fat from beef then wrap in foil and place in freezer for 30 minutes to facilitate slicing.
2. While the meat is in freezer, make sauce by combining lemon juice, wine, shallots, capers, garlic clove, mustard, and parsley. Gradually whisk in the olive oil by pouring in as a small stream, season with salt and refrigerate for at least 20 minutes.
3. Remove the meat from freezer and with a very sharp and thin knife, slice on a diagonal into paper-thin slices.
4. Place the beef slices on platter or individual plates.
5. Drizzle over a little sauce with additional sauce served on the side.
6. Sprinkle the arugula leaves and parmesan cheese over the fillet slices.

Serving suggestion: Serve with either fresh or toasted sliced baguette.

*Note: Substitute red wine vinegar for red wine for non-alcoholic option

Data for 1 serving:

Calories	513	kcal	**Cholesterol**	75	mg
Total Carbohydrates	4	g	**Sodium**	303	mg
Protein	26	g	**Potassium**	506	mg
Total Fat	43	g	**Dietary Fiber**	0.4	g
Saturated Fat	9	g	**Sugar**	1	g
Polyunsaturated Fat	4	g	**Vitamin A**	4%	Daily Value
Monounsaturated Fat	27	g	**Vitamin C**	28%	Daily Value
Trans Fat	0.4	g	**Calcium**	7%	Daily Value
			Iron	19%	Daily Value

CHEESE
& Spinach Dumplings

Once you've made these dumplings, you will be making them again and again... forever. These Italian-inspired dumplings are mouth-wateringly good. The only problem with serving them (especially drenched in butter), is that you won't be able to stop eating them. Feel free to use other leafy greens that may be in season, (or a mixture of a couple) such as kale, chard or beet greens.

These dumplings would also be a fantastic option to serve when you're entertaining: As an appetizer or finger food, they are guaranteed to be a crowd favorite.

Serves: 6		
4	lb	Fresh spinach (large bunches)
		Salt
2	Cup	Ricotta
2		Eggs
1 ½	Cup	Parmesan, freshly grated
¼	tsp	Pepper
¼	tsp	Ground nutmeg
¼	Cup	Plain flour, or just enough to roll dumplings in
6	Tbsp	Butter, melted

1. Wash the spinach and remove the leaves from the stems.
2. Add a splash or two of water with a pinch of salt to the bottom of a large pan over medium to low heat. Add the spinach leaves and cover, allowing the leaves to steam until completely wilted, turning the leaves over a few times.
3. Remove from heat and strain. Once cool enough to handle, squeeze every bit of water out of the leaves with your hands: this is all-important and is the secret of success (otherwise the dumplings would fall apart).
4. Place the well-drained leaves on a large chopping board and finely chop.
5. In a large bowl, mash the ricotta and stir in the eggs, half the parmesan, salt, pepper, nutmeg and the chopped spinach.
6. Work together very well, shape into balls (approximately the size of a walnut) and then lightly roll in the flour (lay enough flour on a plate to roll each ball into).
7. Fill a large saucepan halfway with water, bring to a boil and very carefully drop in the dumplings.
8. Keep the water barely simmering until they rise to the surface; they do so very quickly.
9. Lift them out very carefully with a slotted spoon and serve very hot with melted butter and the remaining parmesan.

Data for 1 serving:

Calories	520 kcal		**Cholesterol**	166 mg
Total Carbohydrates	19 g		**Sodium**	1338 mg
Protein	30 g		**Potassium**	1517 mg
Total Fat	38 g		**Dietary Fiber**	7 g
Saturated Fat	21 g		**Sugar**	2 g
Polyunsaturated Fat	3 g		**Vitamin A**	638% Daily Value
Monounsaturated Fat	12 g		**Vitamin C**	47% Daily Value
Trans Fat	4.9 g		**Calcium**	85% Daily Value
			Iron	65% Daily Value

SIMPLE
Greek Salad

Serves: 6		

Ingredients:

4	Cups	Mixed salad greens: (use whatever you have on hand such as spinach, arugula, kale, watercress, romaine etc)
3	Med	Tomatoes, diced (or 1½ cups cherry tomatoes cut in half)
4		Scallions, sliced
1	Lg	Cucumber, sliced
12		Black ripe olives, pitted
⅓	Cup	Italian dressing

1. Add all salad ingredients to a large serving bowl.
2. Drizzle with dressing and lightly toss together.
3. Allow to stand for up to 15 minutes before serving for flavors to combine.

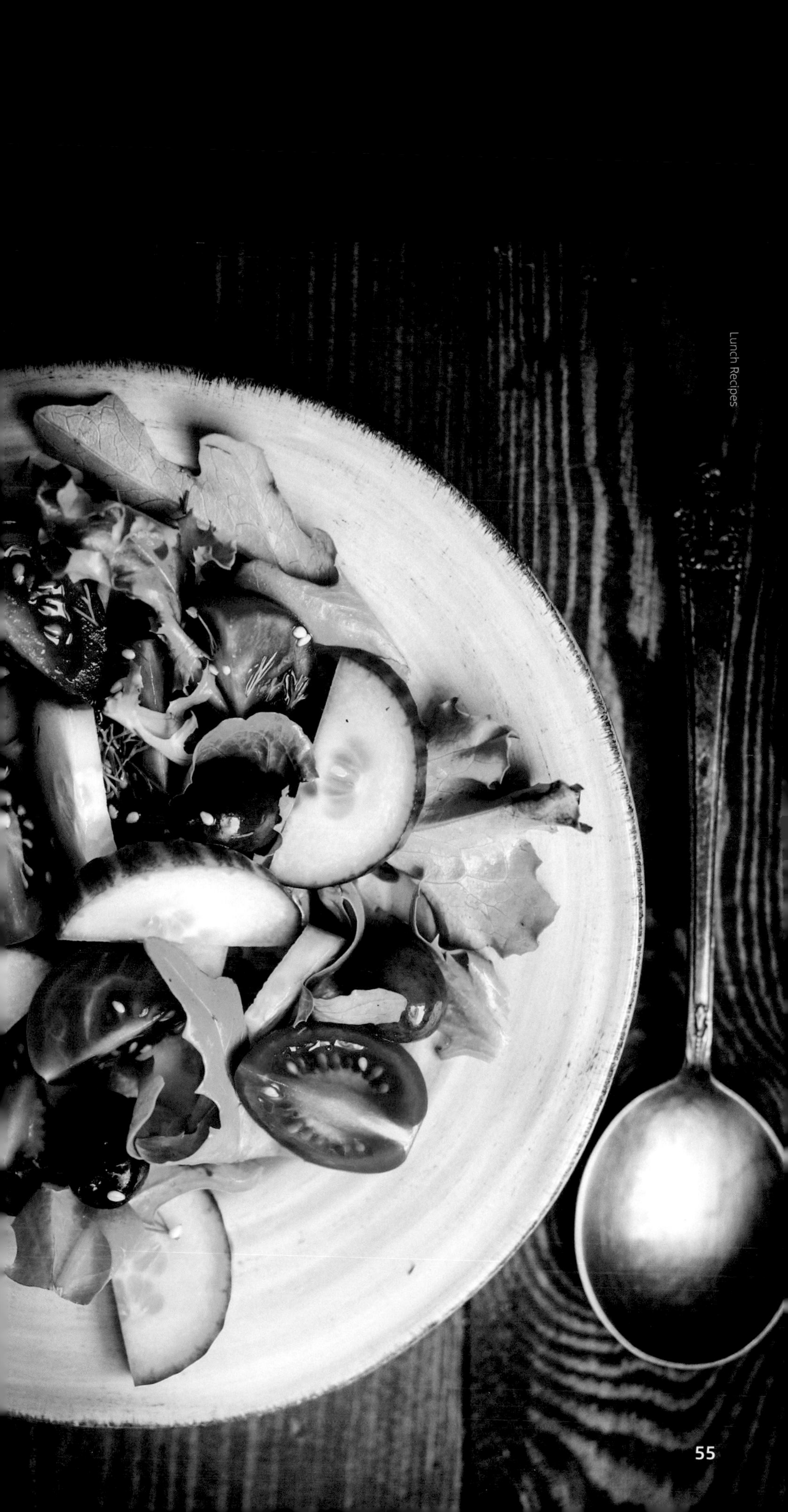

ITALIAN
Dressing

Makes: ¾ cup

Ingredients:

¼	Cup	Capers, drained
1		Garlic clove, minced
1		Scallion, minced
½	Cup	Olive oil
½	tsp	Pepper
1	Sml	Dried red chili, sliced
½	tsp	Fennel seed, crushed
1	Tbsp	White wine vinegar
2	Tbsp	Lemon juice, freshly squeezed

1. Combine all ingredients in a jar with tight-fitting lid and shake well.
2. Store with lid tightly secured in the refrigerator for up to 7 days.

PICKLED HERRING
with Beet Dip Crostini

These crostinis look incredible and taste just as good. They are the perfect combination of flavors, colors and textures. This light, bright and uplifting dish offers a great mix of earthy, sweet and sour flavors, each mouthful offering a taste sensation. If you're after a super quick lunch option we suggest you make the dip ahead of time. Store the beetroot dip in a glass jar with secured lid in the refrigerator for up to 1 week. Any leftover dip can be used as a snack with vegetable sticks or slices of toasted pita bread.

Makes: 8

Dip:

1	lb	Beets, soft cooked, peeled and cut into chunks
4	oz	Labna
1	Tbsp	Apple cider vinegar
2	Tbsp	Shallots, minced
½	tsp	Dry mustard
½	tsp	Dried thyme
½	tsp	Dried tarragon

To serve:

8	slices	Crostini, toasted
1	Tbsp	Olive oil
12	oz	Pickled herring, drained
½		Spanish onion, peeled and thinly sliced
3	oz	Gherkins, thinly sliced
2	Tbsp	Lemon juice, freshly squeezed

1. Brush the crostinis with a little olive oil on each side.
2. Place the crosinis either on a hot grill plate or under a hot broiler and grill on both sides until lightly brown. Remove from heat and set aside.
3. Meanwhile add all the dip ingredients to a food processor or blender and process until smooth.
4. Adjust seasonings, adding more vinegar and salt to taste.
5. Lather each crostini slice with the dip and top with 2–3 slices of the pickled herring, slices of gherkin, slices of the Spanish onion and a squeeze of lemon juice over the top.
6. Serve immediately.
7. Refrigerate any remaining dip in a tightly sealed container for up to 3 days.

Data for 1 serving:

Calories	277 kcal	**Cholesterol**	18 mg
Total Carbohydrates	27 g	**Sodium**	669 mg
Protein	10 g	**Potassium**	247 mg
Total Fat	15 g	**Dietary Fiber**	3 g
Saturated Fat	4 g	**Sugar**	11 g
Polyunsaturated Fat	1 g	**Vitamin A**	11% Daily Value
Monounsaturated Fat	6 g	**Vitamin C**	10% Daily Value
Trans Fat	0 g	**Calcium**	7% Daily Value
		Iron	13% Daily Value

PITA BREADS
with Roasted Lamb & Vegetables

Have you got a crowd to feed? If so, then we have the recipe for you!

Make the succulent lamb ahead of time as it takes a bit to prepare and then cook. Although there is a little time involved getting the lamb ready for serving, it is well worth the wait. At the time of serving, the pita breads will come together in no time at all. This lunch dish is also a fun dish for kids (and anyone for that matter) to make their own, stuffing their pita breads with the lamb and filling ingredients.

Serves: 12

6		White pita breads
For the Lamb:		
3 ½	lb	Lamb shoulder, on the bone
2	Tbsp	Lemon juice
1	tsp	Chili flakes
1	tsp	Ground coriander
1	tsp	Ground ginger
½	tsp	Black pepper, freshly ground
1	Sml	Garlic clove, peeled and crushed
Filling:		
6	oz	Black olives, pitted and drained
2	Med	Tomatoes, diced
1	Lg	Red bell pepper, seeded and sliced
1	Lg	Zucchini, grated
1	Cup	Arugula leaves
¼	Cup	Italian parsley, leaves chopped
1		Red onion, peeled and thinly sliced
2	Tbsp	Lemon juice
1	Tbsp	Balsamic vinegar
1	Tbsp	Olive oil
		Salt and pepper, to taste

60

1. Prepare the lamb the day before.
2. Combine the lemon juice, chili flakes, ground coriander, ginger, black pepper and the crushed garlic. Rub this marinade all over the lamb, place in a roasting tin, cover with cling film and chill in the fridge overnight.
3. The next day, preheat the oven to 400 F. Remove the lamb from the fridge 30 minutes before you want to start cooking it and leave to bring to room temperature.
4. Roast the lamb in the oven for 1 hour 20 minutes for pink lamb, giving it a further 30 minutes if you prefer it well done.
5. When the lamb is cooked, remove it from the oven, cover with foil and let it rest for about half an hour in its tin.
6. Meanwhile prepare all the filling ingredients and gently toss together in a serving bowl.
7. Return to the lamb and, using a very sharp knife, cut the lamb down either side of the bone, trim all the fat and any sinew and discard. Dice the lamb into 1-in cubes.
8. Spoon the lamb and vegetable filling in to each pita bread, season with a little salt and pepper if you wish and serve.

Data for 1 serving:

Calories	526 kcal	Cholesterol	122 mg	
Total Carbohydrates	29 g	Sodium	660 mg	
Protein	35 g	Potassium	538 mg	
Total Fat	30 g	Dietary Fiber	2 g	
Saturated Fat	12 g	Sugar	2 g	
Polyunsaturated Fat	3 g	Vitamin A	25%	Daily Value
Monounsaturated Fat	13 g	Vitamin C	63%	Daily Value
Trans Fat	0.5 g	Calcium	9%	Daily Value
		Iron	25%	Daily Value

RICE
& Lentil Salad

Lentils are so versatile. They are generally added to stews and soups, however, one of our favorite ways to serve them is in this cold, flavorsome Rice and Lentil Salad. This salad is a very simple meal to prepare and is a fabulous lunch option. It could also act as a vegetarian option for an entrée. The balance of fresh herbs and the citrus in the dressing bring this salad alive, while the fennel seeds add a tantalizing flavor. This salad can be made a couple of hours ahead of time and kept in the fridge until ready to serve.

Salad:

2 ½	Cup	Cooked rice, cooled
¾	Cup	Canned green lentils, drained and rinsed
¾	Cup	Canned chickpeas, drained and rinsed
3	Tbsp	Mint, freshly chopped
¼	Cup	Basil, freshly chopped
1		Yellow bell pepper, seeded and diced

Dressing:

¼	Cup	Capers, drained
1		Garlic clove, minced
1		Scallion, minced
½	Cup	Olive oil
½	tsp	Pepper
½	tsp	Fennel seed, crushed
1	Tbsp	White wine vinegar
2	Tbsp	Lemon juice

1. Add all the salad ingredients together in a large bowl and toss lightly together.
2. To make the dressing, combine all dressing ingredients in a jar with tight-fitting lid and shake well.
3. Drizzle your preferred amount of dressing over the salad and toss together again. Store any remaining dressing in jar with lid secured in the refrigerator.
4. Divide among serving bowls and serve immediately.

Data for 1 serving:

Calories	620 kcal	Cholesterol	0	mg
Total Carbohydrates	65 g	Sodium	1057	mg
Protein	10 g	Potassium	378	mg
Total Fat	36 g	Dietary Fiber	7	g
Saturated Fat	5 g	Sugar	2	g
Polyunsaturated Fat	5 g	Vitamin A	25%	Daily Value
Monounsaturated Fat	24 g	Vitamin C	109%	Daily Value
Trans Fat	0 g	Calcium	5%	Daily Value
		Iron	23%	Daily Value

GRILLED SALMON
On Herbed Couscous

When wild salmon comes into season, be sure to put this recipe on the menu. Salmon is somewhat of a firm-fleshed fish, which means cooking the fish fillet under the broiler won't dry out the fish like it would other species.

The rich, strong flavor of the salmon balances wonderfully with the freshness of the herbs in the couscous along with the sweetness from the bell pepper. For a grain and gluten-free alternative you can swap the couscous for cooked quinoa.

Serves: 4

1 ½	lb	Salmon fillets (4x 6-oz pieces)
1	Lg	Zucchini, thinly sliced
2	Tbsp	Olive oil
		Salt and pepper, to taste

Herbed Couscous:

1 ½	Cup	Vegetable stock
¼	tsp	Pepper, freshly ground
1		Bay leaf
1	Tbsp	Thyme leaves, chopped fresh
1	Tbsp	Parsley, chopped fresh
1	tsp	Olive oil
1	Cup	Couscous
½	Cup	Yellow bell pepper, seeded and finely diced
½	Cup	Tomatoes, finely diced

1. For the couscous, combine the stock, pepper, herbs and oil in a small saucepan and bring to a boil.

2. Add the couscous, mix well and then remove from the heat. Cover tightly and allow to stand for at least 5 minutes, or until all of the liquid has been absorbed. Set aside and then mix through the diced bell pepper and tomatoes.

3. Meanwhile rub the surface of the fish with a little olive oil and sprinkle with salt and freshly ground black pepper.

4. Cook under a preheated broiler set at high heat for approximately 3–4 minutes per side or until the fish is cooked through and just flakes with a fork, (do not overcook or the fish will become tough).

5. While the fish is cooking, heat 1 tablespoon of the olive oil in a skillet over medium to high heat. Cook the zucchini until just tender and slightly golden, approximately 5–8 minutes.

6. To serve, place a rounded ½ cup of couscous on each of 4 plates and top with a single piece the cooked zucchini, dividing it equally with a piece of grilled fish on top.

7. Serve with a slice or two of fresh lemon or lime, if desired.

Data for 1 serving:

Calories	441	kcal	**Cholesterol**	113	mg
Total Carbohydrates	39	g	**Sodium**	748	mg
Protein	38	g	**Potassium**	423	mg
Total Fat	14	g	**Dietary Fiber**	4	g
Saturated Fat	3	g	**Sugar**	4	g
Polyunsaturated Fat	1	g	**Vitamin A**	48%	Daily Value
Monounsaturated Fat	6	g	**Vitamin C**	127%	Daily Value
Trans Fat	0.5	g	**Calcium**	9%	Daily Value
			Iron	16%	Daily Value

SHRIMP
& Asparagus Salad

Asparagus and shrimp, a match made in heaven. This Shrimp and Asparagus Salad is incredibly delicious, and drizzled with the creamy horseradish dressing, it is the ideal salad to be serving up in springtime when asparagus is super fresh and plentiful. With minimal and simple ingredients, this salad is easy to make and can be whipped up in less than 10 minutes. This salad is best served immediately while warm and will go perfectly with a glass of white wine such as a Pinot Grigio.

Serves: 4

1	Med	Onion, peeled and diced
2		Garlic cloves, minced
1	Tbsp	Olive oil
1	lb	Asparagus, trimmed and cut in to 1 ½ in. pieces
1	lb	Shrimp, cooked, shelled and deveined
2	Lg	Tomatoes, cut in to wedges

Dressing

1	Cup	Mayonnaise
¼	Cup	Parsley, finely chopped
½	tsp	Pepper, freshly ground
½	tsp	Celery seed
½	tsp	Sea salt
1	Tbsp	Prepared horseradish
¼	Cup	Freshly squeezed lemon juice

To serve

4		Lemon wedges/slices

1. Heat the olive oil in a skillet over medium to high heat. Sauté the onion and garlic for 3–5 minutes, or until tender.
2. Add the asparagus and shrimp and continue to sauté, tossing frequently until the asparagus is barely tender and shrimp is heated through, approximately 2 minutes. Remove from heat and place in a serving bowl, toss through the tomatoes.

3. In another small bowl, mix together the mayonnaise, parsley, pepper, celery seed, salt, horseradish and lemon juice.
4. Stir the dressing into the shrimp and asparagus salad.
5. Divide between serving bowls and serve with a slice of lemon.

Data for 1 serving:

Calories	467 kcal	Cholesterol	242 mg
Total Carbohydrates	26 g	Sodium	1444 mg
Protein	35 g	Potassium	680 mg
Total Fat	26 g	Dietary Fiber	3 g
Saturated Fat	4 g	Sugar	8 g
Polyunsaturated Fat	12 g	Vitamin A	35% Daily Value
Monounsaturated Fat	8 g	Vitamin C	50% Daily Value
Trans Fat	0.1 g	Calcium	2% Daily Value
		Iron	40% Daily Value

SICILIAN
Eggplant Caponata

A traditional and popular eggplant dish that is delicious served with freshly baked crusty bread. This caponata is often served up as an appetizer; however, we love our Sicilian Eggplant Caponata as a lunch option. Place your serving dish of this Mediterranean goodness along with slices of crusty baguette, (or bread of choice) and let everyone dig in. Such a lovely and easy vegetarian meal that is full of flavor and wonderful textures, a wonderful dish to share with friends.

Serves: 8		
1	Lg	Eggplant, cut into 1 in. cubes
2	Tbsp	Olive oil
2	Med	Onions, peeled and diced
2		Garlic cloves, crushed
3		Celery stalks, sliced
1	lb	Canned Italian plum tomatoes
10		Green olives, pitted and quartered
½	Cup	Pine nuts
¼	Cup	Capers
¼	Cup	White wine vinegar
2	Tbps	Sugar
		Salt and pepper, to taste

1. Heat the olive oil in a large non-stick skillet over medium to high heat. Season the eggplant with salt and pepper and cook in skillet in heated oil until tender. When done, remove from pan and set aside.
2. Sauté the onion in the same skillet until tender (add a little more olive oil if necessary). Add garlic, celery, tomatoes, and olives. Reduce heat to medium-low, cook slowly for 10 minutes.
3. Meanwhile heat the vinegar in a small saucepan over medium heat. Stir in the sugar until sugar is dissolved.
4. Return to the skillet, add in the cooked eggplant, pine nuts and capers.
5. Add the vinegar mixture to the skillet with vegetables and mix through.
6. Season with salt and pepper and cook for 5 minutes longer.
7. Serve chilled on top of sliced baguette, grilled crostini, or fresh slices of your preferred Italian-style bread.

Data for 1 serving:

Calories	158 kcal	Cholesterol	0	mg
Total Carbohydrates	13 g	Sodium	441	mg
Protein	3 g	Potassium	375	mg
Total Fat	11 g	Dietary Fiber	4	g
Saturated Fat	1 g	Sugar	7	g
Polyunsaturated Fat	3 g	Vitamin A	8%	Daily Value
Monounsaturated Fat	6 g	Vitamin C	16%	Daily Value
Trans Fat	0 g	Calcium	3%	Daily Value
		Iron	7%	Daily Value

SIMPLE
Marinated Chicken Breasts

These delicious, tender chicken breasts are a great option if you're looking for something to prepare as a quick and easy lunch option ahead of time. Make a batch or two of these breasts at the beginning of your week and have them sliced up ready to go in the fridge for when it comes to serving lunch. Serve them with your preferred side; however, they would pair beautifully with a simple Greek salad or some grilled Mediterranean vegetables.

Serves: 4

2	lb	Chicken breast, skinless, boneless and halved
2		Garlic cloves, minced
2	tsp	Basil, fresh and finely chopped
1	tsp	Thyme, fresh
¼	tsp	Pepper
¼	Cup	White wine vinegar
¼	Cup	Orange juice, freshly squeezed
¼	tsp	Salt

1. Sprinkle chicken on both sides with garlic, basil, thyme and pepper.
2. Arrange chicken in shallow bowl. Mix together the vinegar and orange juice and pour over chicken.
3. Cover and refrigerate for at least 2 hours.
4. Place chicken on a broiler pan and set temperature to 500 F. Arrange oven rack so chicken is about 4 inches from heat.
5. Broil, turning, about 6 minutes per side or until a fork can be inserted in the chicken with ease.
6. Sprinkle with salt, sliced breasts and serve with your favourite side salad.

Data for 1 serving:

Calories	259 kcal	**Cholesterol**	131 mg
Total Carbohydrates	2 g	**Sodium**	266 mg
Protein	52 g	**Potassium**	618 mg
Total Fat	3 g	**Dietary Fiber**	0.2 g
Saturated Fat	1 g	**Sugar**	1 g
Polyunsaturated Fat	1 g	**Vitamin A**	1% Daily Value
Monounsaturated Fat	1 g	**Vitamin C**	19% Daily Value
Trans Fat	0.04 g	**Calcium**	3% Daily Value
		Iron	11% Daily Value

SPINACH
Torta

Looking for an exciting way to get more greens into your belly...? Well this is it. This spinach torta is an easy and extremely tasty way to make sure you're getting your daily dose of greens. Not only does it taste fantastic, it also looks incredibly inviting which hopefully means those fussy eaters won't turn their noses up at the first sign of "green." Each mouthful is not only bursting with flavor, but also plenty of nutrients as well.

Serves: 6

10	oz	Pie crust
1	Tbsp	Dijon mustard
Filling		
¼	Cup	Butter
9	oz	Frozen spinach, thawed and well drained (remove as much liquid as possible)
½	Cup	Red onion, peeled and diced
¼	Cup	Sun-dried tomatoes, without oil, chopped
1	tsp	Italian dried herbs
½	tsp	Dried oregano leaves
¼	tsp	Garlic powder
¼	tsp	Salt
4		Eggs, beaten
2	Cup	Mozzarella cheese, shredded

1. Heat oven to 450 F.
2. Prepare pie crust according to package directions for one-crust baked shell using 10" spring form pan.
3. Place prepared crust in pan, and press into the bottom and up the sides. Spread mustard over bottom of the crust and bake for 9–11 minutes or until crust is lightly browned.
4. Reduce oven to 350 F.
5. Melt the butter in large skillet over medium to low heat.
6. Add spinach, onion and tomatoes. Cook and stir for 5 to 7 minutes or until onion is crisp-tender. Remove from heat, then add the Italian seasoning, oregano, garlic powder and salt. Mix well.
7. In a large bowl, combine the eggs and cheese. Mix well. Stir in spinach mixture until well combined.
8. Spoon evenly into partially baked crust, and bake for 25 to 35 minutes or until golden brown on top.
9. Allow to stand for 10 minutes before removing from pan and slicing.

Data for 1 serving:

Calories	499 kcal	Cholesterol	181 mg
Total Carbohydrates	29 g	Sodium	810 mg
Protein	19 g	Potassium	317 mg
Total Fat	35 g	Dietary Fiber	4 g
Saturated Fat	14 g	Sugar	3 g
Polyunsaturated Fat	5 g	Vitamin A	114% Daily Value
Monounsaturated Fat	12 g	Vitamin C	20% Daily Value
Trans Fat	2.2 g	Calcium	38% Daily Value
		Iron	19% Daily Value

TUNA
Stuffed Eggplants

Eggplant is an extremely versatile vegetable and is the hero of so many Mediterranean dishes, just like this one. While there are many stuffed eggplant recipes, (and why not, who doesn't like a stuffed eggplant?), we love what we have created with this one. Using tuna and anchovies boosts this dish's flavor (and nutritional profile), which is then balanced out beautifully with the feta cheese, capers and olives. If you are after a vegetarian option, substitute the anchovies and tuna for cooked chickpeas or cannellini beans that have been roughly chopped.

Serves: 4		
4	Tbsp	Olive oil
2	Lg	Eggplants
1 to 2	tsp	Sea salt, coarsely grated
2		Tomatoes, diced
1 ½	Cup	Bread crumbs, fresh
7	oz	Canned tuna in water, drained
6		Anchovy filets, finely chopped
2	Tbsp	Capers, minced
1	Tbsp	Basil, finely chopped
1	Tbsp	Italian parsley, chopped
½	Cup	Olives, finely minced
½	Cup	Grated cheese
½	Cup	Feta, crumbled

1. Preheat oven to 375 F.
2. Cut the eggplants in half lengthwise and take out the flesh, leaving a ½" shell. Finely dice the pulp, sprinkle well with salt and place in colander for 30 minutes.
3. Do the same with the eggplant shells: Sprinkle with salt and put them on a paper towel to drain.
4. Heat 4 tablespoons of olive oil in a large skillet. Add the well-drained eggplant pulp and cook until lightly browned. Add the tomatoes and cook the mixture over high heat until the liquid is evaporated.
5. Add in all other ingredients except the grated cheese and feta. Cook the mixture for 2 more minutes.
6. Place the eggplants in a lined baking dish. Fill the eggplant halves with the mixture and sprinkle over the grated cheese and crumbled feta. Place in the oven and bake for 1 hour.

Data for 1 serving:

Calories	602 kcal		Cholesterol	64 mg
Total Carbohydrates	47 g		Sodium	2044 mg
Protein	32 g		Potassium	893 mg
Total Fat	33 g		Dietary Fiber	13 g
Saturated Fat	11 g		Sugar	11 g
Polyunsaturated Fat	2 g		Vitamin A	23% Daily Value
Monounsaturated Fat	13 g		Vitamin C	27% Daily Value
Trans Fat	2.0 g		Calcium	34% Daily Value
			Iron	26% Daily Value

TUSCAN
Tuna Salad

A delicious flavor combination, celebrating all things Tuscany. What really makes this tuna salad sing are the zinging pops of flavor from the capers and the peppery, earthy tones from the arugula. Unlike other salads, you will find this one is very satisfying and filling. Bursting with nutritional goodness, loaded with protein and fiber, this meal will have you feeling on top of the world and keep you going right through to the evening. The recipe is also quite versatile. Feel free to substitute the tuna for other protein sources such as salmon or cooked chicken. You could even just increase the amount of chickpeas and omit the tuna for a vegetarian option.

Serves: 4

14	oz	Canned tuna in water, drained
8	oz	Canned chickpeas, drained and rinsed
1	Lg	Tomato, seeded and diced
1	Sml/Med	Cucumber, halved and sliced
½	Cup	Red onion, peeled and thinly sliced
⅓	Cup	Olives, sliced
2	Tbsp	Capers
3	Cup	Arugula leaves
2	Tbsp	Basil leaves, freshly chopped
¼	Cup	Italian dressing

1. Combine all the salad ingredients together in a bowl and lightly toss together with the Italian dressing.

2. Divide among serving bowls and serve immediately.

Data for 1 serving:

Calories	262 kcal	**Cholesterol**	30 mg
Total Carbohydrates	21 g	**Sodium**	983 mg
Protein	29 g	**Potassium**	605 mg
Total Fat	7 g	**Dietary Fiber**	4 g
Saturated Fat	1 g	**Sugar**	5 g
Polyunsaturated Fat	3 g	**Vitamin A**	19% Daily Value
Monounsaturated Fat	2 g	**Vitamin C**	22% Daily Value
Trans Fat	0.5 g	**Calcium**	8% Daily Value
		Iron	18% Daily Value

TUSCANY SAUSAGE
& Bean Soup

There are times when a salad just won't do for lunch. Those times call for this Tuscany Sausage and Bean Soup. Soup can be a great lunch option that can be made ahead of time and transported easily if you're eating lunch away from home. A comforting, hearty and nourishing meal bursting with flavor (mainly thanks to the addition of Italian sausage and fresh basil), perfect for when the weather is cool, this soup will warm your heart—an excellent comfort food indeed.

Serves: 4

3		Italian sausages, mild
14	oz	Canned cannellini beans, drained and rinsed
2		Celery stalk, sliced
1	Lg	Zucchini, sliced
1	Lg	Carrot, sliced
1	Med	Onion, peeled and diced
3	Cup	Beef stock
8	oz	Tomato purée
3	Tbsp	Fresh basil, freshly chopped
		Salt and pepper to taste
½	Cup	Parmesan, freshly grated

1. Slice sausages ½" thick.
2. Using a large saucepan, brown the sliced sausages on all sides over medium to high heat, then drain off any excess fat.
3. Add the beans, celery, zucchini, carrot and onion. Sauté 2 minutes, stirring.
4. Add the beef stock, tomato purée and basil and mix through, bring to a boil.
5. Reduce the heat to low and allow to simmer uncovered for approximately 30 minutes or until the soup has thickened and the vegetables are tender.
6. Season with salt and pepper to taste.
7. Ladle into bowls and garnish with grated parmesan cheese.

Data for 1 serving:

Calories	443 kcal		**Cholesterol**	43 mg
Total Carbohydrates	39 g		**Sodium**	2070 mg
Protein	25 g		**Potassium**	1303 mg
Total Fat	22 g		**Dietary Fiber**	8 g
Saturated Fat	8 g		**Sugar**	9 g
Polyunsaturated Fat	3 g		**Vitamin A**	108% Daily Value
Monounsaturated Fat	9 g		**Vitamin C**	49% Daily Value
Trans Fat	1.3 g		**Calcium**	22% Daily Value
			Iron	26% Daily Value

DINNER
Recipes

CHICKEN

Piccata

This Chicken Piccata dish is going to be your new favorite chicken dish for sure! Garlic, lemon, butter and chicken... flavor combinations don't get much better than this. The chicken breasts are moist, perfectly served with a generous amount of the sauce poured over the top. The addition of capers bring an extra zing that we think makes this dish absolutely perfect. Serve alongside your preferred seasonal salad or lightly steamed Mediterranean vegetables for a well-balanced meal.

Serves: 6

3	Lg	Chicken breasts, boneless and skinless
		Pepper
⅓	Cup	Flour, to dredge (a little more or less)
¼	Cup	Olive oil
5		Garlic cloves, sliced
¼	Cup	White wine
¼	Cup	Demi-glace, (opt.)
1		Lemon, juiced
½	Cup	Butter
		Parsley, chopped finely

To garnish:

Capers

Lemon slices

Fresh parsley, finely chopped

1. Slice the chicken fillets in half to make 6 fillets altogether. Gently pound the meat with a mallet until thin and flat but not broken. Sprinkle meat with black pepper and dredge lightly in flour.
2. Preheat a heavy wide skillet.
3. Add the olive oil and sauté the garlic until lightly browned, then remove and reserve.
4. Turn up the heat and fry the chicken quickly.
5. Remove the chicken to a serving platter, set aside and keep warm.
6. Drain oil from pan, then deglaze pan with white wine. Add demi-glace if desired, lemon juice and the reserved garlic.
7. Stir well to heat the sauce thoroughly, then add the butter (the garlic can be removed with a slotted spoon or left in).
8. Stir through the parsley and then spoon the sauce over the chicken.
9. Garnish with capers, thin lemon slices and freshly chopped parsley.
10. Serve with your preferred side.

Data for 1 serving:

Calories	463 kcal		**Cholesterol**	170 mg
Total Carbohydrates	7 g		**Sodium**	407 mg
Protein	37 g		**Potassium**	38 mg
Total Fat	32 g		**Dietary Fiber**	0.4 g
Saturated Fat	14 g		**Sugar**	0.2 g
Polyunsaturated Fat	2 g		**Vitamin A**	12% Daily Value
Monounsaturated Fat	15 g		**Vitamin C**	6% Daily Value
Trans Fat	0 g		**Calcium**	1% Daily Value
			Iron	2% Daily Value

FALAFELS
in Tortillas with Tahini Sauce

This is an excellent recipe for when you are entertaining. There is something so amazing about getting together around a table of food with loved ones for a meal and this meal is perfect for just that.

Get out your best serving ware and fill your bowls with all that is required for your dinner guests (even if this is just you and your family)

to make these delicious falafel tortillas. This recipe is also extremely versatile; feel free to use a mixture of leafy greens such as arugula or spinach leaves with the addition of sliced cucumber, bell peppers or even some grilled eggplant would go wonderfully. A lovely way to use fresh, local, seasonal produce.

Serves: 6

1 ½	lb	Canned chickpeas, drained and rinsed
½	tsp	Baking powder
2	tsp	Ground cinnamon
2	tsp	Ground cumin
1	bunch	Parsley, finely chopped
1	Med	Onion, grated
4		Scallions, minced
2	Tbsp	Cilantro, chopped
		Oil, for deep frying
To serve		
6	Med/Lg	Tortillas, or pita bread warmed
1 ½	Cup	Mixed lettuce leaves
1 ½	Cup	Cherry tomatoes, cut in half
6		Lemon wedges
Tahini Sauce		
⅔	Cup	Tahini (sesame paste)
3	Tbsp	Water (as needed)
2		Lemons, juiced
2		Garlic cloves, minced
2	Tbsp	Fresh parsley, minced
		Black pepper

1. Remove the skins from the chickpeas by rubbing them with a dish towel.
2. Place the chickpeas in a food processor and purée them.
3. Add the garlic, baking powder, coriander, cumin, parsley, onions, scallions, and cilantro. Blend the ingredients together so that a smooth paste is formed (add a little more water if necessary).
4. Let the mixture rest for 30 minutes.
5. Meanwhile make the tahini sauce. In a small bowl place the tahini, water, and lemon juice. Mix the ingredients together so that a smooth sauce is formed (add more water if necessary).
6. Add the garlic, parsley, and black pepper; mix so that they are well blended. Set the sauce aside.
7. In a medium/large saucepan place the enough oil into pot for deep frying (approximately 2–3 cups) and heat it on medium high until it is hot.
8. Using a small ice cream scoop, scoop the falafel mixture and drop into the hot oil, and deep-fry them for 2–3 minutes, or until they are golden brown.
9. Drain them on paper towels.
10. In each of the pita breads lay down a bed of lettuce, topped with cherry tomatoes and falafel. Squeeze over some lemon juice and top with the tahini sauce.

Data for 1 serving:

Calories	668	kcal	**Cholesterol**	0	mg
Total Carbohydrates	61	g	**Sodium**	707	mg
Protein	16	g	**Potassium**	466	mg
Total Fat	42	g	**Dietary Fiber**	12	g
Saturated Fat	6	g	**Sugar**	3	g
Polyunsaturated Fat	13	g	**Vitamin A**	20%	Daily Value
Monounsaturated Fat	8	g	**Vitamin C**	38%	Daily Value
Trans Fat	0	g	**Calcium**	18%	Daily Value
			Iron	31%	Daily Value

FISH
in Island Sauce

Simple, light and healthy dishes can at times create the most comforting and satisfying meal. This recipe is versatile, using your preferred fish of choice. Try and choose a fish that is available fresh and local. Grouper does go well; however, any white-fleshed fish will taste just as good.

The perfect balance of flavors along with the pops of zing from the capers will leave you hanging for more. This delicate, yet delicious dish can be served up within 20 minutes of opening the refrigerator door.

Serves: 6		
6		Fish fillets, (preferably grouper)
3	Tbsp	Olive oil
6		Garlic cloves, minced
2		Onions, peeled and diced
20	oz	Canned diced tomatoes, strained
1		Green pepper, seeded and diced
½	Cup	Capers, drained
2	Tbsp	Parsley, finely chopped
2	Tbsp	White wine vinegar
1		Bay leaf

1. Heat the oil in a large skillet over medium to high heat. Cook the garlic until golden.
2. Add the fish fillets and cook on each side until golden and cooked through, approximately 3 minutes on each side. Fish will flake with a fork when done.
3. Remove the fish from skillet, set aside and keep warm.
4. Add the onion to skillet and sauté until transparent.
5. Add the tomato and the pepper. Continue to sauté until the flavor peaks.
6. Add the capers, parsley, vinegar and laurel.
7. Cook on low heat for 10 minutes. Pour the salsa over the fish fillets and serve immediately.

Data for 1 serving:

Calories	223 kcal		**Cholesterol**	61 mg
Total Carbohydrates	10 g		**Sodium**	696 mg
Protein	26 g		**Potassium**	235 mg
Total Fat	9 g		**Dietary Fiber**	2 g
Saturated Fat	1 g		**Sugar**	4 g
Polyunsaturated Fat	1 g		**Vitamin A**	16% Daily Value
Monounsaturated Fat	5 g		**Vitamin C**	55% Daily Value
Trans Fat	0.4 g		**Calcium**	7% Daily Value
			Iron	13% Daily Value

FREGULA
with Clams and Chilis

Shellfish is not only an important and popular part of a Mediterranean Diet, it is also a pivotal part of a nutritionally dense diet. You are able to use any type of small clams, cockles or mussels. Select local live produce where possible for superior taste and freshness.

When cooking shellfish, be sure to not overcook as shellfish can become quite rubbery if cooked for too long. If you are unable to get hold of fregola to use for this recipe, Israeli cous cous will be a great substitute.

Serves: 6		
4	Tbsp	Olive oil
1	Med	Red onion, peeled and thinly sliced
4		Garlic cloves, peeled and thinly sliced
2	oz	Prosciutto, in ⅛" dice
1	lb	Tiny clams, cockles or manilas (scrubbed and rinsed)
1	Cup	White wine, dry
1	Cup	Chicken stock
1	Pinch	Saffron
½	Cup	Tomato purée
1	Tbsp	Chili flakes
1	lb	Fregola
1	bunch	Italian parsley, leaves removed but left whole

1. Cook the fregola according to package instructions until just cooked, approximately 15 minutes.
2. In a 12" to 14" frying pan or saucepan, heat olive oil to smoking over medium high heat.
3. Add onion, garlic and prosciutto and sauté until softened.
4. Add clams, white wine, saffron, chicken stock and tomato purée and bring to a boil. Cover and cook for 5–8 minutes until clams/cockles/mussels have opened, discarding any that haven't.
5. Once done, add the cooked fregola to clam pot and cook a little longer until texture resembles risotto.
6. Add chili flakes and stir through.
7. Serve, season with salt and pepper and garnish with a generous amount of parsley.

Data for 1 serving:

Calories	511 kcal	**Cholesterol**	31 mg	
Total Carbohydrates	68 g	**Sodium**	451 mg	
Protein	23 g	**Potassium**	584 mg	
Total Fat	13 g	**Dietary Fiber**	5 g	
Saturated Fat	2 g	**Sugar**	4 g	
Polyunsaturated Fat	2 g	**Vitamin A**	16%	Daily Value
Monounsaturated Fat	8 g	**Vitamin C**	31%	Daily Value
Trans Fat	0.2 g	**Calcium**	3%	Daily Value
		Iron	69%	Daily Value

MEATLOAF
Stuffed with Prosciutto & Cheese

Meatloaf must be one of the best comfort foods around! We have created a Mediterranean-inspired meatloaf stuffed full of prosciutto and creamy mozzarella. This meatloaf requires a tiny bit more effort than a regular meatloaf; however, that little extra effort will be so worth it!

As soon as you take a bite and get some of that creamy melted mozzarella, paired perfectly with the prosciutto, along with the Mediterranean flavors from the vegetables and herbs, we guarantee you won't be trying another meatloaf recipe anytime soon.

Serves: 6

1 ¼	lb	Ground beef
1	Lg	Onion, finely chopped
1	tsp	Prepared mustard, preferably dijon
10	oz	Tomato soup, canned
2	Tbsp	Parsley, chopped fresh
1		Green bell pepper, seeded and finely chopped
2	Lg	Eggs, lightly beaten
1	Cup	Bread crumbs
⅛	tsp	Salt
⅛	tsp	Black pepper
1		Garlic clove, minced
½	tsp	Dried oregano

Stuffing:

6–8	slices	Prosciutto
1	Cup	Mozzarella cheese, shredded

1. Preheat oven to 400 F.
2. Lightly oil a 9"x5"x3" pan.
3. In a large bowl, combine all the meatloaf ingredients, adding more bread crumbs if necessary, one tablespoon at a time, to make a firm loaf.
4. Lightly spray a large piece of aluminium foil or non stick baking paper. Place the meat mixture on the foil, and form into a 12"×8" rectangle.
5. Arrange the prosciutto on top of the meat, leaving a small margin around the edges. Sprinkle shredded cheese on top of the prosciutto slices.
6. Starting from the short end, carefully roll the meat mixture jelly-roll style. Seal the edges and ends. Place the loaf seam side up in the prepared pan.
7. Bake 1 hour or until done.
8. Serve with your choice of steamed vegetables or side salad.

Data for 1 serving:

Calories	446 kcal		**Cholesterol**	153 mg
Total Carbohydrates	28 g		**Sodium**	990 mg
Protein	32 g		**Potassium**	758 mg
Total Fat	22 g		**Dietary Fiber**	3 g
Saturated Fat	9 g		**Sugar**	8 g
Polyunsaturated Fat	1 g		**Vitamin A**	20% Daily Value
Monounsaturated Fat	8 g		**Vitamin C**	62% Daily Value
Trans Fat	1 g		**Calcium**	20% Daily Value
			Iron	25% Daily Value

MEDITERRANEAN
Meatballs

When you think of Mediterranean meals, classic meals such as spaghetti and meatballs may come to mind. We have emphasized the Mediterranean with these meatballs, creating the most wonderfully delicious, yet easy sauce.

This dish is full of classic Mediterranean vegetables such as eggplant, zucchini, bell peppers, and tomatoes, giving this meal not only a power punch in the nutritional department but making it rich and strong in flavors too. You can guarantee serving this somewhat simple and enjoyable pasta dish at your dinner table will have even the fussiest eaters coming back for more.

Serves: 6

Sauce

2		Garlic cloves, minced
2		Onions, peeled and diced
2		Green peppers, seeded and diced
2		Zucchini, diced
1	Lg	Eggplant, peeled and cubed
4		Tomatoes, peeled and chopped
4	Tbsp	Parsley, freshly chopped
		Salt and pepper
½	tsp	Dried thyme
½	Cup	Chicken stock

Meatball Mixture

1 ½	lb	Ground beef
2	slices	Bread
¼	tsp	Nutmeg
⅓	Cup	Parmesan cheese
1		Egg, lightly beaten
2–4	Tbsp	Olive oil
		Salt and pepper, to taste

To serve:

Cooked spaghetti, (or pasta of choice)

Parmesan cheese

Fresh parsley, chopped

1. In a large skillet or saucepan, prepare your sauce by sautéing the garlic in olive oil over medium to high heat.
2. Add the onion and continue to sauté.
3. Add in the green peppers, zucchini, eggplant, and tomatoes. Continue to cook and then add parsley, salt and pepper, thyme and chicken stock. Reduce heat and allow to simmer for approximately 40 minutes uncovered to make a thick sauce.
4. Add the bread to a food processor and pulse a few times until it resembles crumbs; set aside.
5. Beat the egg slightly and set aside.
6. In a large bowl mix the nutmeg, salt and pepper and parmesan cheese into the ground meat.
7. Roll into balls and then dip the balls into egg and then into bread crumbs; set aside.
8. Heat 2–4 tablespoons of olive oil in a large skillet over medium to high heat. Add the meatballs, fry on each side for approximately 6–8 minutes until golden brown, remove from pan and drop into sauce, and gently stir through.
9. Pour the sauce with meatballs over cooked spaghetti.
10. Sprinkle with more parmesan cheese if desired and garnish with fresh parsley.

Data for 1 serving:

Calories	555	kcal	**Cholesterol**	115	mg
Total Carbohydrates	43	g	**Sodium**	328	mg
Protein	33	g	**Potassium**	1072	mg
Total Fat	28	g	**Dietary Fiber**	7	g
Saturated Fat	9	g	**Sugar**	8	g
Polyunsaturated Fat	2	g	**Vitamin A**	25%	Daily Value
Monounsaturated Fat	14	g	**Vitamin C**	94%	Daily Value
Trans Fat	1	g	**Calcium**	17%	Daily Value
			Iron	26%	Daily Value

NEAPOLITAN
Polenta Pie

This hearty and flavorsome Neapolitan Polenta Pie is a great way to serve up polenta a little differently. It will quite possibly become your *favorite* way to serve up polenta.

There is a little time involved in making the "cheese" for this recipe; however, if time does not allow, you may be able to find some delicious, creamy ready-made labna from most good delis. Once you have the "cheese" ready to go, this meal comes together very easily. This is definitely comfort food at its finest, hearty and loaded with traditional flavors we all love. We guarantee this meatless Mediterranean dish will become a firm family favorite.

Serves: 4		
12	oz	Greek yogurt, plain
1	Cup	Polenta
3	Cup	Water
1	tsp	Sea salt
1 ½	Cup	Pizza sauce
1	Cup	Red onion, peeled and thinly sliced
¼	lb	Field mushrooms, washed and sliced
2	oz	Dried porcini mushrooms, soaked
3	Tbsp	Capers
1		Tomato, sliced
1	Cup	Green bell pepper, seeded and sliced
⅓	Cup	Parmesan cheese, grated
⅓	Cup	Basil, freshly chopped

1. The day before serving, prepare "cheese" from yogurt by mixing yogurt with ½ teaspoon salt and placing it in a strainer lined with several layers of cheesecloth.
2. Squeeze cloth very gently around yogurt and place in the strainer over a bowl. Refrigerate and drain for at least 10 hours.
3. Before continuing with recipe, carefully remove cheesecloth from the ball of cheese.
4. Bring the water to a boil in a saucepan and stir polenta into the boiling water.
5. Add ½ teaspoon salt, cover and cook over low heat, stirring frequently for 15 minutes or until thick and soft.
6. Pour into a 9-inch non-stick pie plate or casserole dish and spread evenly over bottom and sides.
7. Preheat oven to 425 F.
8. Spread pizza sauce over polenta.
9. Arrange vegetables over sauce, top with yogurt cheese, capers and the parmesan cheese. Bake for 25 minutes or until pie is bubbling hot throughout.
10. Remove from oven and top with basil.

Data for 1 serving:

Calories	272	kcal	**Cholesterol**	23	mg
Total Carbohydrates	35	g	**Sodium**	1412	mg
Protein	18	g	**Potassium**	749	mg
Total Fat	7	g	**Dietary Fiber**	9	g
Saturated Fat	4	g	**Sugar**	13	g
Polyunsaturated Fat	1	g	**Vitamin A**	52%	Daily Value
Monounsaturated Fat	1	g	**Vitamin C**	192%	Daily Value
Trans Fat	1	g	**Calcium**	18%	Daily Value
			Iron	31%	Daily Value

ORANGE BAKED
Fish with Onions & Mushrooms

Local fresh wild-caught fish is a staple of the Mediterranean Diet and we have the perfect recipe to compliment any white-fleshed fish that may be in season. This dish is full of delicate sweet flavors, while also offering the perfect balance of savory notes. This one-pan dish is surprisingly simple, and the minimal preparation and hands-on time means you can sit down and enjoy some wine while the dish cooks itself. Serve straight from the oven with fresh crusty buttered bread, delicious!

Serves: 4		
6		Pearl onions, peeled and cut in quarters Small chopped green onions
1	lb	Mushrooms, sliced
1 ½	lb	Flounder, or fish of choice (fresh, local and wild caught)
		Salt and pepper, to taste
1	tsp	Dried Italian herbs
2	Tbsp	Olive oil
½	Cup	White wine
¼	Cup	Orange juice
3	Tbsp	Curacao liqueur
1	tsp	Paprika
2	Tbsp	Parsley, freshly chopped

1. Layer half of the onions and mushrooms in a greased 9-inch baking pan or casserole dish.
2. Lay the fish on top of the vegetables and sprinkle with salt, pepper and Italian herbs.
3. Add remaining onions and mushrooms over the top.
4. In a small bowl/jar combine the olive oil, white wine, orange juice and curacao, then pour over vegetables and fish.
5. Cover and bake at 350 F for 40 minutes or until the fish is opaque and the vegetables on top are slightly golden.
6. Sprinkle with paprika and parsley, and serve immediately.

Data for 1 serving:

Calories	405 kcal	**Cholesterol**	163 mg	
Total Carbohydrates	13 g	**Sodium**	214 mg	
Protein	54 g	**Potassium**	434 mg	
Total Fat	10 g	**Dietary Fiber**	2 g	
Saturated Fat	1 g	**Sugar**	8 g	
Polyunsaturated Fat	1 g	**Vitamin A**	8%	Daily Value
Monounsaturated Fat	5 g	**Vitamin C**	84%	Daily Value
Trans Fat	0 g	**Calcium**	1%	Daily Value
		Iron	5%	Daily Value

PORTUGUESE
Chorizo Soup

This is an excellent comforting soup that is full of flavor, vibrant in color and perfect for the colder months. The chorizo sausage is certainly the star of this recipe, giving this dish a wonderfully spicy flavor while the potato adds a rustic and hearty addition.

Make a double batch of this soup (if the ingredients you have allow for it) and freeze a batch for leftovers so that you have a ready-made meal for those nights you can't be bothered to cook.

Serves: 6		
2	Tbsp	Olive oil
1	Cup	Onion, peeled and diced
8	oz	Chorizo sausage, thinly sliced
2	tsp	Garlic, minced
2	Cup	Potatoes, peeled and sliced
4	Cup	Chicken stock
4	Cup	Water
		Salt and pepper, to taste
½	lb	Kale, leaves torn from stems and leaves sliced
½	lb	String green beans, trimmed and sliced in half lengthways

1. In a medium to large soup pot, heat 2 tablespoons of the olive oil over medium. Add in the onions and garlic and cook for 2 to 3 minutes until soft and transparent, (don't allow them to brown).

2. Add the chorizo and potatoes, continue to sauté for a further 5–10 minutes, or until the potatoes are slightly golden and the sausage is browned.

3. Pour in the stock and water and boil gently over medium heat for 15 minutes.

4. Add in the kale and string beans, leave uncovered, reducing the heat to low. Simmer for 5 minutes.

5. Season with salt and pepper and then ladle into bowls and serve.

Data for 1 serving:

Calories	309 kcal	**Cholesterol**	23 mg
Total Carbohydrates	28 g	**Sodium**	899 mg
Protein	12 g	**Potassium**	692 mg
Total Fat	17 g	**Dietary Fiber**	6 g
Saturated Fat	5 g	**Sugar**	3 g
Polyunsaturated Fat	1 g	**Vitamin A**	132% Daily Value
Monounsaturated Fat	4 g	**Vitamin C**	122% Daily Value
Trans Fat	0.8 g	**Calcium**	13% Daily Value
		Iron	15% Daily Value

ROASTED LAMB
Rack with Velvet Black Olive Sauce

This roasted rack of lamb with velvety olive sauce is a dish you want to bring out when you have an impression to make.

The lamb will melt in your mouth perfectly and pairs wonderfully with the rich, smooth and dreamy black olive sauce. The sauce takes a little time to prepare, so pour yourself a glass of wine and enjoy your moment in the kitchen cooking with love, knowing you're about to create a masterpiece your dinner guests will cherish.

Serves: 4

Sauce

4		Garlic cloves, peeled and crushed
4		Shallots, peeled and chopped
1	Tbsp	Black peppercorns
½	Cup	Butter, unsalted
2	Cup	Madeira wine
2	Cup	Red wine
1	Sml	Rosemary sprig
1	Med	Tomato, diced
1	Cup	Demi-glace*
½	Cup	Nicoise olives, pitted
		Salt and pepper, to taste

Lamb

2		Lamb racks, 8 chops on each
1	Tbsp	Olive oil
		Salt and pepper, to taste
1		Rosemary sprig, leaves only, chopped

*or good quality lamb or beef broth

The sauce:

1. In a large skillet over medium heat sauté the garlic, shallots and peppercorns in 1 tablespoon of butter until lightly browned.
2. Add the Madeira and red wine, rosemary and tomato.
3. Simmer until reduced by two-thirds, leaving approximately 1 cup total.
4. Add the demi-glace and return to a boil. Whisk in remaining butter a little at a time until it is incorporated.
5. If you would like a thicker, richer sauce simply add a little more butter.
6. Strain the sauce through a fine strainer, then transfer to a blender.
7. Add half the olives and purée until almost smooth.
8. Roughly chop the remaining olives, add to the sauce and mix through.
9. Season with salt and pepper to taste, then set aside in a warm place until serving time.

The lamb:

1. Rub the racks well with olive oil and season with salt, pepper and rosemary.
2. Set aside and allow the lamb to come to room temperature.
3. Heat a roasting pan or large sauté pan until very hot.
4. Add a few drops of oil and sear the lamb racks in it on all sides until brown.
5. Place the racks bone side down in the hot pan and transfer to a 400 F oven. Roast to medium rare, or to desired doneness, 10 to 20 minutes.
6. Allow the lamb to rest for 15 minutes, then slice into 8 chops per rack.
7. Serve 4 chops to a plate, accompanied with sauce and served with vegetables of choice.

Serving suggestion: serve with garlic mashed potatoes and lightly cooked vegetables of your choice.

Data for 1 serving:

Calories	1247	kcal	**Cholesterol**	340	mg
Total Carbohydrates	29	g	**Sodium**	1656	mg
Protein	88	g	**Potassium**	1384	mg
Total Fat	61	g	**Dietary Fiber**	1	g
Saturated Fat	26	g	**Sugar**	12	g
Polyunsaturated Fat	4	g	**Vitamin A**	22%	Daily Value
Monounsaturated Fat	23	g	**Vitamin C**	12%	Daily Value
Trans Fat	0.5	g	**Calcium**	9%	Daily Value
			Iron	44%	Daily Value

STUFFED
Baked Squid

Meals don't get much more "Mediterranean" than this Stuffed Baked Squid.

For an authentic Mediterranean dish you will want to try and source the freshest local squid available as this will provide the best flavor. If fresh squid is not available, you can also make this recipe using large frozen (but then thawed) squid tubes.

This dish is bursting with wonderful fresh flavors from all the herbs, along with an underlying sweetness from the currants. Keep this recipe up your sleeve next time you want to wow your dinner guests.

Serves: 4

3	lb	Squid, fresh (large)
¼	Cup	Olive oil
1	Cup	Onion, peeled and coarsely chopped
⅓	Cup	Rice, long-grain
⅓	Cup	Pine nuts
2	Lg	Garlic cloves, chopped
¼	Cup	Currants
1	Cup	Dry red wine
		Salt and freshly ground pepper, to taste
¾	Cup	Parsley, chopped fresh
¼	Cup	Dill, chopped fresh dill
¼	Cup	Mint, chopped fresh
2	Cup	Canned diced tomatoes

1. Preheat oven to 350 F.
2. Wash and the clean the squids. Grasp the head just below the eyes and pull it off from the rest of the body, set aside.
3. Cut away the thin purplish membrane on the outside of the tail section. Using your index finger, scoop out and discard the guts and thin cartilage "icicle" on the inside of the tail section. Rinse tail sections inside and out and set aside in a colander to drain.

4. Take the head section in one hand and put pressure with your thumb and forefinger around the mouth and eyes, to squeeze them out. Discard the mouth and eyes.

5. Chop the squid tentacles and have them ready, as they will be used in the stuffing.

6. In a large skillet, heat half the olive oil and sauté onion until soft.

7. Add rice, tentacles, and pine nuts and sauté over medium-low heat for 2–3 minutes.

8. Add garlic and currants to rice and stir quickly with a wooden spoon.

9. Pour in ¼ cup wine and ¼ cup water. Season with salt and pepper. Reduce heat to low and simmer, covered, until liquid is almost completely absorbed and rice is soft but only about half cooked, approximately 15 minutes. 5 minutes before removing skillet from heat, add parsley, dill and mint.

10. Remove and let cool enough to handle.

11. Using a small teaspoon or a butter knife, carefully fill about three quarters of each squid with the rice mixture.

12. Use toothpicks to secure closed.

13. Pour remaining olive oil into a large casserole dish.

14. Place squid carefully in dish and pour in remaining wine, canned tomatoes and just enough water to cover (if required), season with salt and pepper.

15. Cover and place in the oven to cook for 1½ to 2 hours or until the rice is cooked and squid is fork-tender.

16. Check throughout cooking to see if more water is necessary so that the mixture doesn't dry out.

17. Serve squid with a simple green salad.

Data for 1 serving:

Calories	558 kcal	Cholesterol	583 mg
Total Carbohydrates	25 g	Sodium	323 mg
Protein	43 g	Potassium	1074 mg
Total Fat	26 g	Dietary Fiber	3 g
Saturated Fat	4 g	Sugar	6 g
Polyunsaturated Fat	7 g	Vitamin A	17% Daily Value
Monounsaturated Fat	13 g	Vitamin C	57% Daily Value
Trans Fat	0.8 g	Calcium	13% Daily Value
		Iron	21% Daily Value

TURKEY
Barley Soup

If you're looking for a no-fuss recipe and one that can easily use up leftovers, this one is for you. Don't let your leftover turkey meat (chicken meat is also a great option here) go to waste—instead turn it into a fabulous soup with vegetables and barley. The barley in this soup balances out the celery and carrot well, while the parsley gives this soup a lovely fresh flavor.

Being a slow cooker recipe, there is minimal effort required and it's a great way to get a dinner ready by "setting and forgetting". You will be able to put your soup on to cook in the morning, walk out that door and come home to an aroma-filled kitchen that will smell absolutely delicious!

Serves: 4

8	Cup	Chicken stock
1 ½	Cup	Cooked turkey breast, diced
1	Cup	Pearl barley
1		Onion, chopped
2		Celery stalks, chopped
3		Carrots, sliced
1		Bay leaf
1	tsp	Dry thyme
¼	tsp	Dried marjoram
¼	tsp	Ground black pepper
2	Tbsp	Parsley, chopped fresh
		Salt and pepper, to taste

1. Combine all the ingredients in a large soup pot or slow cooker.
2. Cook over low heat in the slow cooker for 6 hours or simmer on the stove for 1 hour, or until the carrots are tender and the barley is soft.
3. Ladle between four serving bowls, season with salt and pepper to taste and serve with warm crusty bread if desired.

Data for 1 serving:

Calories	294 kcal	**Cholesterol**	32 mg	
Total Carbohydrates	51 g	**Sodium**	2031 mg	
Protein	19 g	**Potassium**	632 mg	
Total Fat	3 g	**Dietary Fiber**	10 g	
Saturated Fat	0.4 g	**Sugar**	5 g	
Polyunsaturated Fat	0.3 g	**Vitamin A**	172%	Daily Value
Monounsaturated Fat	0.3 g	**Vitamin C**	11%	Daily Value
Trans Fat	0.3 g	**Calcium**	6%	Daily Value
		Iron	14%	Daily Value

TUSCAN
White Bean Stew

A quick and easy stew and surprisingly full of flavor considering the simple ingredients and the lack of effort required, this meal is ready for you to devour within 20 minutes. It's the perfect mid/late week dinner (or any other time you may be short on time).

Feel free to play around with this recipe by either using different varieties of beans or adding in some leafy greens like kale or chard. If you prefer a little spice, adjust the chili flakes and paprika to taste.

Serves: 6		
1	Tbsp	Olive oil
1	tsp	Garlic, minced
2		Anchovy fillets, chopped
½	tsp	Paprika
½	tsp	Dried chili flakes
1	Cup	Chicken broth
14	oz	Canned crushed tomatoes
1	Cup	Cabbage, shredded or diced
1	Lg	Green bell pepper, seeded and chopped
2	tsp	Lemon juice, freshly squeezed
1 ½	Cup	Canned white beans, drained and rinsed
4	oz	Pasta, (such as farfalle) cooked to packet directions
		Salt and pepper, to taste
		Oregano, freshly chopped
		Parsley, freshly chopped

1. Heat oil in a large pan over medium-high heat.
2. Stir in garlic, anchovies, paprika and chili flakes. Heat for approximately 30 seconds.
3. Add the cabbage and bell pepper and sauté for another 1–2 minutes until cabbage is slightly limp.
4. Add the crushed tomatoes, stock, lemon juice and drained beans.
5. Reduce the heat to medium–low and allow to simmer uncovered for 10–15 minutes.
6. Meanwhile, cook the pasta to packet directions.
7. Serve on hot pasta and garnish with chopped oregano and parsley.

Data for 1 serving:

Calories	168 kcal		Cholesterol	3 mg
Total Carbohydrates	27 g		Sodium	539 mg
Protein	9 g		Potassium	312 mg
Total Fat	3 g		Dietary Fiber	7 g
Saturated Fat	0.5 g		Sugar	1 g
Polyunsaturated Fat	1 g		Vitamin A	14 % Daily Value
Monounsaturated Fat	2 g		Vitamin C	55 % Daily Value
Trans Fat	0.05 g		Calcium	10 % Daily Value
			Iron	18 % Daily Value

DRINK
Recipes

SUN
Smoothie

Yield 1 Serving   **Active Time** 5 Mins   **Total Time** 5 Mins

Ingredients

- » 1 cup of almond milk
- » ½ cup of orange juice
- » ¼ cup of wheat germ
- » 1 banana

This vitamin boosting smoothie is perfect for a hot afternoon... the best part? It's incredibly easy to make. Place all four ingredients in a blender. Blend on high until smooth!

FRQSTY
Fruit Smoothie

Yield 1 Serving   **Active Time** 5 Mins   **Total Time** 5 Mins

Ingredients

- » 1 banana
- » 1 cup strawberries, frozen
- » 1 cup orange juice
- » Mint (optional)

Combine all ingredients into a blender, and purée on high speed. Serve immediately and enjoy a cold, sweet drink full of nutrients. Top with a mint leaf.

FRUIT
Detox Water

Yield 1 Serving   **Active Time** 5 Mins   **Total Time** 5 Mins

Ingredients

- » 2 cups water
- » Sliced cucumber
- » Sliced lime
- » Sliced grapefruit
- » Sprig of rosemary

Simply place all the ingredients in a cup and fill with water. Let soak for up to 5 minutes for the flavors to set in. Continue to refill the glass with water until you're satisfied. Another trick is to adapt the recipe for an entire jug. You can leave the jug in the fridge for up to a day... this is a great detoxing substitute for fruit-flavored soda. Try with soda water for an even better substitute!

SUGAR-FREE
Blueberry Lemonade

Yield 3–4 drinks   **Active Time** 5 Mins   **Total Time** 5 Mins

Ingredients

- » 1 ½ cups lemon juice
- » ½ cup powdered stevia (sugar substitute)
- » 6 cups water
- » 1 cup blueberries
- » ¼ cup mixed fresh herbs, such as basil, mint and tarragon
- » 1 cup cold sparkling water

Pour lemon juice into a pitcher and combine stevia until dissolved. Add water and stir well. Mash blueberries and herbs in a bowl with a wooden spoon. Add to cup and pour lemonade on top. Garnish with whole blueberries and mint.

GREEK
Yogurt Smoothie

Yield 2 Serving   **Active Time** 5 Mins   **Total Time** 5 Mins

Ingredients

- » ⅓ cup Greek yogurt
- » ½ ripe banana, frozen
- » ⅓ cup blueberries, frozen
- » ½ cup spinach, frozen
- » ¼ cup almond milk

Blend all the ingredients together until smooth and creamy. Garnish with extra berries and a sprig of mint, if desired.

DATE
Horchata

Yield 6 Servings   **Active Time** 10 Mins   **Total Time** 10 Mins

Ingredients

- » 1 cup rice
- » 6 cups water
- » 1 cup almond milk
- » ½ cup dates
- » 1 ½ teaspoons vanilla extract
- » 1 cinnamon stick
- » 1 tablespoon maple syrup (optional)

Soak the rice in 2 cups of hot, but not quite boiling, water, for two hours. Rice should come out soft but still raw. Drain and add to a blender. Add the remaining 4 cups of water, dates, vanilla, and the cinnamon. Blend for about 1 minute. Test for sweetness, and add more dates or maple syrup as needed.

Pour the mixture into two bowls. Cover each bowl with a very thin towel or cheesecloth. Strain the mixture out until only the pulp remains. Now, stir in the milk and whisk. Transfer over to a pitcher with a lid. Serve over ice.

SNACK
Recipes

HOMEMADE
Tahini Sauce

Yield ½ cup   **Active Time** 20 Min   **Total Time** 20 Min

Ingredients

- » ½ cup hulled sesame seeds
- » 2-4 tablespoons olive oil
- » Pinch of salt

Grind sesame seeds in a food processor and gradually add oil until smooth. Mix in a pinch of salt.

TIP: Lightly toast the seeds on a stovetop for a deeper, nutty flavor. Don't toast the seeds in the oven as they can easily burn.

CREAMY
Tahini Hummus

Yield 3 Cups   **Active Time** 20 Min   **Total Time** 20 Min

Ingredients

- » ¼ cup tahini
- » ¼ cup lemon juice or the juice of a large lemon
- » 2 tablespoons olive oil
- » 1 garlic clove
- » ½ teaspoon cumin
- » ½ teaspoon salt
- » 1 ½ cups of canned or cooked chickpeas
- » 2–3 tablespoons water
- » Dash of paprika
- » Fresh veggies, sliced

In a food processor, combine the tahini and lemon juice. Slowly add the olive oil, garlic, cumin, and salt. Add the rinsed chickpeas. Add water if hummus is too thick. Serve with a drizzle of olive oil and paprika. Use veggies to dip!

BEETROOT
Hummus

Yield 1 ½ cups   **Active Time** 10 min   **Total Time** 50 min

Ingredients

- » 1 red beet
- » 2 cloves garlic
- » 2 tablespoons olive oil
- » 1½ cups cooked or canned chickpeas, drained and rinsed
- » 2 tablespoons tahini
- » 2 tablespoons lemon juice
- » 3 tablespoons warm water
- » ½ teaspoon cumin
- » ½ teaspoon coriander
- » Salt and black pepper to taste

Preheat your oven to 400 F. Wrap the beet in foil with the garlic and olive oil. On a baking sheet, roast for 30 minutes or until the beet is fork-tender. Leave out to cool... then remove the beet skin. Place the beet in a food processor and blend while adding the rest of the ingredients. Keep in the fridge until ready to use. Serve with veggies!

MEDITERRANEAN
Hummus Stuffed Peppers

Yield 6 Servings   **Active Time** 10 Min   **Total Time** 30 Min

Ingredients

- » 3 bell peppers
- » ½ cup of hummus
- » ¼ cup black olives, sliced
- » ¼ cup feta cheese, crumbled
- » Parsley

Preheat the oven to 500 F. Cut the top of the peppers and scoop out seeds. Place the peppers on a sheet pan and cook for 30–40 minutes, until the skins are completely wrinkled and the peppers are charred, turning them twice while roasting. Scoop hummus into each pepper and garnish with olives, feta cheese and a sprinkle of parsley.

CHICKPEA
Salad

Yield 1 large salad   **Active Time** 15 Min   **Total Time** 15 Min

Ingredients

Salad

- » 1 can chickpeas
- » ½ cup sundried tomatoes
- » ½ cucumber, diced
- » ½ cup of olives, sliced
- » ½ cup red onion, diced
- » ¼ cup parsley
- » ¼ cup feta, crumbled

Dressing

- » ¼ cup of olive oil
- » 2 tablespoons red wine vinegar
- » ½ teaspoon cumin
- » Salt & pepper

Drain the can of chickpeas and add tomatoes, cucumbers, onion, olives, parsley and feta. Combine the dressing ingredients. Refrigerate both for an hour before combining and serving.

APPLE SLICES
with Almond Butter

Yield 6 Pieces   **Active Time** 10 Min   **Total Time** 10 Min

Ingredients

- » 1 apple
- » ¼ cup almond butter
- » 2 tablespoons sliced almonds
- » 2 tablespoons walnuts
- » Small handful dark chocolate chips

Slice the apple into thin strips. Spread with almond butter and top with sliced almonds, walnut chunks and dark chocolate chips.

CHILI LIME
Roasted Chickpeas

Ingredients

- » 1 can chickpeas, rinsed and drained
- » 2 tablespoons olive oil
- » 1 teaspoon chili powder
- » ½ teaspoon cumin
- » 1 lime zested
- » ¼ teaspoon garlic powder
- » ¼ teaspoon salt

Preheat oven to 400 F. Spread chickpeas on a baking sheet in a single layer. Drizzle beans with olive oil and bake for 30 minutes. Mix the rest of the ingredients together and sprinkle over the chickpeas. Serve warm.

Chickpeas are so versatile in the Mediterranean Diet—you'll never have too many chickpeas in your pantry going unused. They can be used in all sorts of recipes and are an amazing source of protein and fiber as well as a very healthy source of carbohydrates. They also contain several key vitamins and minerals such as iron, zinc, vitamin B-6, magnesium, protein and fiber.

TIP: For extra crunchiness, peel chickpeas before roasting and adjust baking time to 45 minutes.

PLAIN GREEK
Yogurt and Fresh Berries

Yield 1 Serving   **Active Time** 5 Mins   **Total Time** 5 Mins

Ingredients

» 1 cup Greek yogurt
» ½ cup strawberries, blueberries, raspberries
» Mint (optional)
» Oatmeal (optional)

Simply throw in your favorite fresh berries and you'll have a delicious and nutritious snack. Add in some oatmeal to turn it into a complete breakfast!

FROZEN
Blueberry Yogurt Swirl Pop Cups

Yield 8 Popsicles   **Active Time** 5 Min   **Total Time** 5 Hours

Ingredients

» 2 cups blueberries

» 2 tablespoons agave/honey

» 1 drop of liquid stevia

» 2 cups Greek yogurt

» 8 wooden craft sticks

Blend the blueberries in a food processor or blender until smoothie-like. Pour into a bowl and gently mix in the agave or honey, stevia, and yogurt. Pour mixture into a popsicle mold and insert wooden craft sticks. Freeze 5 hours and run under warm water to get the popsicle out of the mold.

FROZEN
Chocolate Bananas

Yield 12 Banana Pieces   **Active Time** 20 Min   **Total Time** 5 Hours

Ingredients

- » 4 bananas
- » ⅓ cup almond butter
- » ¼ cup dark chocolate

- » ½ cup chopped almonds
- » 8 wooden craft sticks

Cut bananas into small 2- or 3-inch-long segments. Stick the wooden craft sticks into the bottom of each chunk. Freeze the bananas for about 3 hours. Spread almond butter over the whole banana then freeze for another hour. Melt chocolate in a double boiler, dip each banana piece into the chocolate and roll over chopped almonds. Freeze again until the chocolate is firm, another 1–2 hours.

TIP: Substitute cashews or walnuts for almonds.

CHOCOLATE
Chia Pudding with Raspberries

Yield 4 Servings   **Active Time** 15 Min   **Total Time** 8 Hours

Ingredients

» 1 ½ cups almond milk
» ¼ cup dark chocolate
» 3 tablespoons chia seeds
» ¼ cup raspberries
» ¼ cup almonds
» Mint leaves (optional)

Add 1 cup of milk and the chocolate to a pot and melt down the chocolate slowly, making sure not to scald the milk. Stir in the remaining milk and let cool to room temperature. Pour chocolate mixture into a glass and fold in chia seeds. Let stand for 15 minutes before stirring again. Leave covered in refrigerator for at least 8 hours. Stir the chia seed mixture and top with raspberries, almonds, and mint leaves.

CHIA SEED
& Mango Purée with Blueberries

Yield 2 Servings   **Active Time** 15 Min   **Total Time** 2 ½ Hours

Ingredients

» ¼ cup chia seeds
» 1 ½ cups almond milk
» 1 tablespoon honey or agave
» 1 drop liquid stevia
» ½ teaspoon vanilla extract
» 1 mango
» ½ cup blueberries
» Mint leaf

Mix the chia seeds, milk, honey or agave, stevia, and vanilla extract in a bowl until combined. Allow the chia seed mixture to soak for 2 hours. Purée the mango in a food processor or blender. Fold mango purée into the chia seed mixture. Garnish with blueberries and mint.

CARAMELIZED
Pear with Gorgonzola

Yield 2 Servings   **Active Time** 20 Min   **Total Time** 45 Min

Ingredients

- » 1 ripe pear, sliced
- » 3 tablespoons honey or agave
- » ¼ cup gorgonzola cheese
- » 2 tablespoons olive oil
- » ¼ cup natural caramel sauce (see recipe)
- » Sprouts (optional)

Heat olive oil in pan over medium heat. Add the pear and cook until lightly browned. Add in the gorgonzola cheese. Continue cooking until the cheese begins to melt. Serve on a plate and garnish with caramel sauce and sprouts.

NATURAL
Caramel Sauce

Yield 1 jar   **Active Time** 20 Min   **Total Time** 20 Min

Ingredients

- » ¼ cup water
- » ¼ cup butter
- » 6 tablespoons powdered erythritol
- » 2 tablespoons maple syrup
- » ¾ cup heavy cream

In a pot mix the water, erythritol and syrup. Simmer on medium heat until the water starts to boil. Add the butter and whisk for about 10 minutes until the mixture begins to brown. Turn off the heat and add in the cream. Turn the heat to medium-high and whisk for 2 minutes. Once the sauce begins to thicken and gets the consistency of caramel sauce, turn off the heat. Feel free to serve immediately or store in a jar for up to 2 weeks.

CHOCOLATE
Cookies

Yield 2 dozen   **Active Time** 20 Min   **Total Time** 30 Min

Ingredients

- » 1 cup olive oil
- » 1 tablespoon vanilla extract
- » 2 ½ cups Swerve (sugar replacement)
- » 1 teaspoon salt
- » 1 large egg
- » 2 cups flour
- » ½ teaspoon baking soda
- » 2 cups unsweetened chocolate chips

Preheat oven to 350 F and prepare two baking sheets with parchment paper.

Combine the oil, vanilla, Swerve, and salt in a large bowl until smooth. Mix in egg. In a separate bowl, combine flour and baking soda. Combine wet and dry ingredients. Fold in chocolate chips.

Form dough into 1-inch balls and then slightly press onto baking sheet, leaving room for cookie to expand.

Bake until cookies are golden brown around the edges, about 10 minutes. Cool on a rack, serve.

LEMON
Bars with Tahini Crust

Yield 12 bars   **Active Time** 30 Min   **Total Time** 2 Hours

Ingredients

Tahini Crust

» ½ cup rolled oats
» ½ cup sesame seeds
» ¼ teaspoon salt
» 8 dates
» ¼ cup tahini

Lemon Filling

» 1 tablespoon arrowroot starch
» 1 cup lemon juice
» 5 tablespoons Swerve (sugar replacement)
» 14 ounces firm tofu
» ¼ tablespoon lemon zest

Preheat oven to 350 F and line a baking sheet with parchment paper. Add the oats and sesame seeds to a food processor, pulse for 30 seconds. Add the salt, dates, tahini and blend until combined, about 90 seconds. Press the mixture down into the baking dish until distributed and well-packed. Bake until edges are golden brown, about 15 minutes.

Blend arrowroot starch, lemon juice, Swerve, tofu, and lemon zest until smooth. Pour onto baked crust and cook for an additional 35 minutes. Let cool, then refrigerate for about 90 minutes until the custard is set.

MEDITERRANEAN
Chocolate Chips Muffins

Ingredients

- » 1 cup of Swerve (sugar replacement)
- » A pinch of salt
- » 3 tablespoons + ⅓ cup of olive oil
- » 3 eggs
- » 1 tablespoon vanilla extract
- » 1 cup of all purpose flour
- » 1 tsp of baking powder
- » 1 ½ cups dark chocolate chips

Instructions:

Preheat the oven to 350 F. In a large bowl, combine the Swerve, salt and 3 tablespoons of olive oil. Mix at a low speed until creamy. Incorporate the remaining olive oil.

Continue mixing at a low speed and add eggs one at a time. Add the vanilla extract. Sift in the all-purpose flour and baking powder. Mix well. Fold in chocolate chips.

Line muffin tin with paper cups or lightly grease with olive oil. Divide the batter into cups and bake for 15 minutes, until a toothpick can be removed cleanly.

Tip: Personalize your muffins with additional toppings such as hazelnuts, almonds, or even almond butter.

PISTACHIO
Pudding

Yield 6 dishes   **Active Time** 30 Min   **Total Time** 5 Hours

Ingredients

- » 1 cup pistachios, unsalted and shelled
- » ½ cup Swerve (sugar replacement)
- » 2 cups + 2 tablespoons almond milk
- » 3 eggs
- » 2 tablespoons maple syrup
- » Dash of salt
- » 2 tablespoon olive oil
- » ¼ tablespoon vanilla extract

Blend the pistachios in a food processor until finely ground. Add ¼ cup Swerve and 2 tablespoons of almond milk. Pulse until a paste forms. In a saucepan, combine the paste and remaining 2 cups of almond milk. Cook over medium-high heat until the mixture begins to steam.

In a food processor, add in the remaining Swerve, 1 whole egg, 2 egg yolks, maple syrup and salt. With the processor still running, slowly add ½ cup of the warm mixture to temper the eggs so that the mixture does not curdle.

Slowly add the contents of the food processor into the pan and continue to cook. Reduce the heat to medium and cook until the pudding begins to bubble and thicken. Remove from heat before adding the oil and vanilla. Divide into 6 serving cups, and chill for about 4 and a half hours. Serve cold with chopped pistachios as garnish.

peap